GERONIMO

Allan Houser

# GERONIMO

## *The Last Apache War Chief*

*by* EDGAR WYATT

*Illustrated by Allan Houser*
*Direct Descendant of Geronimo*

Whittlesey House
McGRAW-HILL BOOK COMPANY, INC.
*New York London Toronto*

GERONIMO



*Library of Congress Catalog Card Number:* 51–13610

NINTH PRINTING

Published by Whittlesey House
A division of the McGraw-Hill Book Company, Inc.
Printed in the United States of America

# Contents

# GERONIMO

See the *Guide to Pronunciation of Indian Names* printed at the back of the book.

CHAPTER I

# Apache Boy

The trail wound through forests of cactus and mesquite. Gokliya rode beside Nolgee, a young Apache warrior.

"Our allies are the deserts and mountains," said Nolgee. "They protect us from our enemies."

"I know," said Gokliya. "I have heard this from every brave who has ridden this trail with me."

Nolgee smiled. "You will hear it many times more, Gokliya. You will repeat it many times, yourself, when you are a warrior training boys for the hunt and the warpath. You must never forget it. The mountains are our fortresses. The deserts reveal any enemy who comes close to them."

Gokliya was twelve years old now, and Nolgee was his teacher. Nolgee taught him to make bows and lances. Gokliya learned to creep so silently through the forest that he could almost touch a grazing deer before it leaped away. He learned to bring down rabbits and wild turkeys with whirling sticks. He could gallop beside a thundering buffalo and find its heart with one thrust of his spear.

Many Apache braves had helped to train Gokliya for the warpath and the hunt. Now it was Nolgee who rode with him through the mountains and far out across the desert. They studied every peak and every pass through the hills. Gokliya knew each rock, each tree, each clump of prickly pear. He knew every desert water hole—which ones held water all the year and which were dry in summer. Nolgee showed him where hollow rocks lay on the hillsides.

"They catch the rain," said Nolgee. "Someday, the water may save your life."

Now the two Apaches left the flat Arizona desert and climbed through rocky canyons. Their wiry ponies trotted easily up the twisting, narrow trail. Far above them, in a high mountain valley, was the camp of the Bedonko band of Warm Springs Apache Indians. Here Gokliya lived with his mother, Juana, and his seven brothers and sisters.

When he was born in June, 1829, Juana had called him Gokliya—He Who Yawns. Years later, he would be named again by his Mexican enemies. They would call him Geronimo—a name that blazed across the whole Southwest. That name brought a thrill of fear to every desert ranch and village, to Americans and Mexicans alike. Someday, the world would know Geronimo.

But today, as he rode beside Nolgee toward the Indian village, no one knew Gokliya except the Indians in his own Apache band.

"You learn quickly, Gokliya," said Nolgee. "Someday, you will be a fine warrior. Your father would be proud if he had lived."

Gokliya flushed with pleasure. Praise from Nolgee was the highest praise.

"Nolgee," he said, "tell me. Ah-Nay says that all our enemies will soon be driven away. Our chiefs win many victories. No one can stand against them. Ah-Nay says there will be no enemies left to fight when we are warriors. Is this true?"

Nolgee smiled at the boy's serious face. "Your friend Ah-Nay speaks with a foolish tongue. Our enemies are stronger as each moon passes. Many miners dig red iron near Santa Rita. More ranchers than ever crowd the valleys. More Mexican soldiers ride through our deserts and mountains. They no longer pretend to be friendly. Their rifles bark the instant they see an Apache."

Nolgee shook his head. "Ah-Nay is wrong. There will be battles for you to fight, Gokliya."

Their ponies finished the long climb. They rode through a narrow pass and looked down on the wickiups of their people. A mountain stream ran sparkling through the grassy valley. The Indian village dozed in the afternoon sun. Babies slept in their cradleboards, swinging from the low branches of oak trees. Grazing war ponies whisked away the flies that stung their flanks.

"We will not ride together tomorrow, Gokliya," said Nolgee. "Mangas leads the warriors away at dawn." He turned toward his wickiup.

"Will there be a raid?" called Gokliya eagerly.

Nolgee shrugged. "Mangas has not said. Perhaps it will be only a hunt. You and I will ride again when I return."

Gokliya waved, then his heels touched his pony's flanks. He galloped down the slope and sped past the other wickiups. He splashed through the little stream and rode easily up the steep face of a cliff beyond. Soon he came to the edge of the forest that spread across the top of this mountain range.

The warriors had been gone for a week. When Nolgee was away, Gokliya and his friends, Ah-Nay and Kunya, ran races through the mountain trails and played their war games. They built a wickiup of their own in the forest.

They cut tall saplings and stripped off the branches. They sharpened the end of each sapling with their knives. Then they drove them into the ground, making a circle of poles. Near the top, they pulled the poles almost together and tied them with strips of leather. This left a space for the smoke to escape as it rose from the fire hole they dug in the floor. Between the poles they stretched buckskin and wove grass and the leafy branches of trees.

Alope, an Apache girl, often played with them in the forest. She brought skins for the floor and walls of the wickiup. She drew pictures of antelope, deer, and bears on the buckskin walls.

"This is our village," said Alope, "and you are the warriors who defend it."

Kunya and Ah-Nay sat on rocks nearby, polishing their bows and lances. Gokliya fitted a sharp tip of bone to a three-foot arrow.

"The warriors have been away for seven days," said Gokliya. "Maybe there has been a battle. We should be with them. I am tired of games and make-believe."

"Boys cannot be warriors," said Alope.

"Gokliya wants to be a chief, not just a warrior," said Ah-Nay. "Like his grandfather, Maco. Like our own Mangas Coloradas."

"Gokliya will never be as great as Mangas." Kunya laughed. "Mexican soldiers flee at the sight of Mangas. He could kill ten, even twenty, all alone. Who runs when Gokliya comes with his bow and arrow? Only the rabbits."

Gokliya smiled at the teasing boys. He knew that Alope was right. Still, it was hard to wait.

"Look! Look!" called Alope. She pointed to the mountain peaks where lookouts stayed day and night. "There is smoke on the peaks!"

The boys sprang to their feet. Their eyes followed Alope's pointing finger. Puff after puff of smoke rolled upward from the peaks. Then a long steady stream of white smoke rose against the bright blue of the sky.

"The warriors are coming!" shouted Gokliya.

They raced down the steep hillside and leaped

*"There is smoke on the peaks!"*

across the little stream. Alope dashed into the wickiup of her people. Gokliya burst panting into his own. His mother was piling wood into the fire hole.

"The warriors are coming!"

"I know." His mother went on with her work. "I can read smoke, too, Gokliya."

"They will bring ponies and mules and much game, maybe. Maybe they fought great battles. Maybe——"

"So many maybes." She put a strong brown arm around Gokliya. "Be quiet—there is something that I must tell you."

Her voice was troubled. "Last night I woke from my sleep. I heard an owl hoot near our camp."

Gokliya looked anxiously at his mother. All Apaches knew that owls were evil. Spirits lived in the owls. Their hooting warned an Apache band that trouble or danger was near.

"Among the warriors are many of our kinsmen. Your cousin, Mora, is with them."

"Yes," said Gokliya stoutly. "He is the finest warrior——"

"Hush. The owl's hoot says that not all our warriors will return. If our kinsmen have been lost, we must be brave."

"We must be brave," Gokliya repeated. "If my cousin is lost, I will take his place."

His mother smiled. "In a few years, maybe. Now run and bring water for my cooking. The men will be hungry."

CHAPTER 2

# Feast of Victory

Excitement ran through the camp of the roving Apache band. The women dressed themselves in their softest doeskin. They colored their cheeks and bound back their hair. The old men who could no longer hunt and fight came out of their wickiups and stood in silent groups. The wounded warriors who had been left behind stood with them.

Shouting children raced through the village, their dogs yelping at their heels. The smoke still rose in a thin straight line from the distant peaks. The warriors were coming!

Every eye was on the narrow pass that led between high cliffs. The warriors must come that way. It was the only pass into this valley.

"Here they come! Here they come!" shouted the children.

Through the pass came the Apache braves. They rode in single file down toward the wickiups of the people. Mangas, their chief, came first. His great body was proudly erect. Then the sub-chiefs came and then the warriors, one by one.

The youngest warriors came last, driving nine—ten—eleven mules. There was a great canvas pack tied to the back of each mule. A murmur ran through the crowd of waiting Indians. The mules had been captured in some distant raid. The warriors were bringing them to the people.

Gokliya stood beside his mother, remembering the warning of the hooting owl. Not all the warriors would return. She held his arm tightly, straining her eyes to recognize the warriors.

Her hand fell away from Gokliya's arm. "I see Mora and all our kinsmen. They are safe."

"I have counted forty braves," said Gokliya. "Forty-one left with Mangas."

He looked at each face as the war-painted braves rode nearer. Then he whispered, "It is Coyote who is lost—Alope's uncle."

Gokliya looked toward Alope's wickiup. She had stood there a moment ago, beside her mother and father. She had been dancing with excitement. Now they were gone. Gokliya knew that they had counted the warriors, too. They would stay inside their wickiup while the others feasted and danced.

There was no time to think of Alope now. The

braves drove the captured mules into the circle of waiting Indians. The braves smiled at the cheering people. They swung the canvas packs to the ground. Proudly they unrolled them.

The people gasped with delight. There were great sacks of sugar, coffee, and beans. There were cooking vessels of tin and iron and bolts of bright gingham and calico. There were many rifles and ropes and a few saddles. The warriors smiled as the people ran to look at pile after pile of booty. This had been a fine raid.

The women hurried to prepare a feast. The boys gathered wood for great fires. A mule—the Apaches' favorite meat—was killed. Juicy chunks went into the steaming kettles.

When the feasting was over, dancers leaped and twisted in the flickering firelight to the beat of buckskin drums. Then the warriors rose, one by one. Each told of his part in the raid.

Gokliya's eyes were shining. He could almost see the rich Mexican wagon train driven by many men. He could see the cunning ambush as the warriors described it. He could hear the shrill war cries and the pounding war ponies as they raced to the attack.

Gokliya watched the gestures of each speaker. They told of the wild gallop around the huddled wagons. They told of clouds of arrows and the bark

*The dancers leaped and twisted in the firelight*

and whine of rifles. Gokliya's nostrils could almost feel the sharp burning powder.

The warriors told of the last desperate stand of the guards. They laughed as they told how the soldiers had run away in panic, leaving many dead in the canyon.

After all the sub-chiefs and warriors had spoken, a great cry went up from the Indians. They called for their chief.

"Mangas! Mangas! Mangas Coloradas!"

The great chief rose. The firelight cast a huge shadow behind him. Most Apaches were only 7 or 8 inches above 5 feet tall. Mangas stood 6 feet 4. His head was enormous. Feathers in his headband made him seem even taller. His powerful brown body glistened.

His name—Mangas Coloradas—means Red Sleeves in Spanish. Like many Apaches, Mangas had taken a name given him by his Mexican enemies. These enemies said that Mangas was so terrible in battle that his arms were often splashed red with blood to his shoulders.

Mangas spoke quietly at first. He spoke of the fallen warrior, Coyote. He had been the fiercest one in battle. He had led the last wild charge against the wagon train. A dozen bullets had cut him down. "His spirit has joined the spirits of our fathers who died in other battles," said Mangas. "Like them, he lives in our memory."

Now Mangas spoke of his other warriors. He praised each one by name.

"No wonder our enemies tremble. No wonder they flee when we attack. Such warriors as you will drive them away. Someday, you will drive them back to the south from whence they came."

Mangas's voice stopped. The echo of his words was lost in the wild cheering. The dancers flung themselves about the campfire.

The fires burned low and the shadows between the wickiups were black and deep.

Suddenly, another great fire sprang up. In the bright new light every face turned to look. Gokliya jumped up, startled. Then he stood still.

Alope's wickiup was blazing. The flames raced through the woven grasses and branches. They licked at the roof and leaped high. They curled the buckskin walls.

No Indian moved. None raced for water. Even the children understood and were quiet. Coyote's people had set this fire themselves. His home must be destroyed. Everything he owned, all his weapons, must be left to burn. Otherwise, his spirit might come back to the place where he had lived.

Gokliya saw Alope and her parents walking

slowly away. They crossed the little stream and disappeared into the shadows. Tomorrow they would build another home on the other bank. Gokliya turned and walked home at his mother's side.

"Someday," he said, "I will lead such a raid. I will avenge the death of Coyote."

"Someday, perhaps," his mother said. "But now it is time for sleep. Even warriors must sleep."

CHAPTER 3

# The Medicine Man's Story

Gokliya's chest grew broad and deep. The muscles of his arms and legs were lean and strong. His black eyes were sharp.

Time passed—although it seemed to Gokliya that time crawled by like a sluggish Gila monster. In June he would be seventeen.

Now more of their Mexican enemies crowded the Apache country. There were more copper mines in the hills. Mexican soldiers rode with the wagon trains that brought food and tools to the miners. They guarded the copper ore that rolled south to the cities of Mexico.

Mangas fought them with all his strength. His braves raced through the mountain passes. They struck at mines and ranches. They left Apache Pass lined with burned-out wagons.

When the warriors were away, wise old Delkey often came down from his cave and spoke to the people as they sat around their campfires.

Delkey's cave was high on a mountain peak. There, he said, the spirits of Apache chiefs who had fallen in battle came to visit him. They told him of victories to come, said Delkey, and they warned him of danger. Only a medicine man dared to speak to a spirit. No one else could see one.

When Delkey spoke to the people, they crowded close to listen. His tales were of wars and danger and great adventures. Sometimes he told the glorious story of the Apache Nation. Gokliya had heard this story many times—all Apache children must know it. But he thrilled again with pride every time Delkey told it.

Delkey's deep black eyes glowed. His voice rose, sometimes, to a great shout. Often it was deep and proud. When he told of the ancient glory of the Apaches, his story always began in the same way.

"A thousand snows have melted since The People came to this land. Many harvests have come and gone. Nobody knows how many. The wisest men have forgotten the number."

Gokliya sat hugging his knees as he listened. Slowly, Delkey's words went on. His long thin arm pointed far away toward the northwest.

"Long ago, The People lived in the white land of the North. They lived where Ghost Face spreads the sheets of ice that never melt. The People did not like this place of always-snow. They burned their wickiups and marched away to seek the sun.

"The People marched out of the fields of snow. They came through the northern forests. They passed across the land of the broad plains. They

marched by paths that led to many wars. In front, the warriors fought their way. Many enemies attacked them but none could stop The People.

"At last, Usen, the Great Spirit, led them to this land. They found these mountains where the deer were many. They found much game and pleasant streams and the warm sun in summer.

"Usen said to The People—'This is your land.'

"This land Usen gave to us. He gave us the great deserts that are all around us. He gave us these high mountain fortresses. Usen created this land for The People. The People he created for this land. Each he created for the other.

"No enemy shall take it from us!"

Gokliya's eyes blazed with pride.

Delkey's story went on. He told of many enemies who had tried to take this land from the Apaches. He told of battles long ago against the armies of Spain.

These were strange bearded white men. They rode north from Mexico on the first horses that Apaches ever saw. They wore glittering armor and they carried banners of red and gold. Men on foot came with them. These walking men were dressed in long brown robes. They spoke of a strange God.

Many other Indian tribes were friendly with the Spanish soldiers. The Pimas and Papagos learned to pray to the white man's God. The Pueblos were baptized by the brown-robed missionaries.

Apaches were never friends of the Spaniards. They were not baptized.

"Our fathers prayed only to Usen," said Delkey proudly.

The Apaches quickly learned that Spanish horses did not eat Indian boys, as the men in armor claimed. They raided the Spanish corrals and soon began to raise war ponies of their own.

At last, Delkey said, the bearded white men were defeated. They marched away to the south, but the Apache country was not peaceful long. Now Mexico claimed the deserts and mountains from Texas to California. Their soldiers came to drive the Apaches from the land that Usen had given them. "This is the war The People fight today," said Delkey.

The old medicine man finished his story and turned to go back to his cave. He looked down at Gokliya who sat silently with the other boys. Delkey spoke directly to the young Apache.

"You will live long, Gokliya. Someday, you will be a chief among The People. You will be greater than Maco, your grandfather. Your warpath will never end."

He put a bony hand on Gokliya's black head.

"Soon we may have new enemies. The Pinda-Lick-O-Yi, the White-Eyes, are coming from the east."

Gokliya had never seen an American, but tales had reached the Apache camp of white men who trapped beaver on the rivers. They heard of other Americans who traded with the Mexican miners near Santa Rita.

If white men came to crowd the Apache country—Delkey understood this dimly—the time would come when Apaches would have to go. Or their whole way of life would have to change.

Apaches lived as their desert home and their long history forced them to live. Apaches had always roved and raided. They were not farmers. They never stayed long enough in the few fertile spots to learn much of farming. They were scornful of ranchers—"grandmothers of cattle" they called them. Apaches were not weavers. For blankets and much of their clothing they depended on war or trade with their neighbors.

Before the invaders came, the mountains of the Apache country were alive with game. The Indians could get all the meat they needed by hunting deer and elk and buffalo. They traded some of the skins to other tribes for grain and blankets.

But first the Mexicans, and now a few Americans, invaded the hunting grounds with noisy rifles. Meat was scarce. Game was frightened away. The Apaches had few hides to trade. Now they could only get along by raiding the things that they must have to live.

"If more white men come," said Delkey, "they, too, will be our enemies. Be strong, Gokliya. Be brave for the wars that you must fight."

CHAPTER 4

# Gokliya, the Warrior

Gokliya's great day was near. Soon it would be time to test him for the warpath. The braves would take him on four hunts. Then the chiefs would say whether he was ready to join the council of warriors.

Now his training was stern and hard. Nolgee gave him no rest.

He ran short, swift races with Ah-Nay and Kunya. They ran long 4-mile races over the roughest mountain trails. In these long races, each boy took a mouthful of water at the start. He carried the water in his mouth until the race was over. He learned to breathe easily and not to gasp for air.

Nolgee taught them to ride at a tearing gallop, using only their knees to guide their ponies. They used both hands to shoot their arrows or to throw their lances.

Finally, each boy was sent alone into the desert.

Gokliya carried no food or water. He lived for fourteen days on what he could find to eat and drink. He killed a rabbit when he could, or ate the cactus fruit or the wild berries that grew on the mountains. He cut open the thorny barrel cactus and chewed its moist flesh when he was thirsty. Each night, wrapped in his blanket, he listened to the screams of prowling coyotes. Lying on his back, he watched the brilliant desert stars until he fell asleep.

After two weeks, Gokliya returned to the Apache village and reported to Nolgee. The next day they went to Mangas.

"Gokliya is ready," said Nolgee proudly. "My work is done. He knows the arts of war. He knows the secrets of the desert and mountains."

"And the other boys," asked Mangas. "What of Ay-Nay and Kunya?"

"They are ready too."

*"Enju,"* said Mangas. "Good. When you hunt again in the northern canyons, let the boys go with you."

As he rode with the warriors on his first hunts, Gokliya learned quickly that the life of an Apache brave was not all excitement and war. Much of it was work.

When the hunters made camp, the boys watered and fed their horses. They scoured the rough foothills for wood. They built the fires and cooked for the men. They stood guard all night. The braves gave them many tasks. The boys must not grumble. They must not even speak unless some brave asked a question. It was all a part of their test.

Gokliya could not tell whether the braves were pleased with him. They seemed not to notice the boys. They spoke to them only to give them sharp orders.

Now the third hunt was over. Gokliya walked with Ah-Nay along the stream outside the Apache village. They skipped flat stones across the water and squatted where the pools were deep to watch the speckled trout.

There was a shout from the village. Kunya ran toward them.

"We start our fourth hunt tomorrow," said Kunya. "Fifty warriors will go. Mangas himself will lead us!"

"This will be more than a hunt, maybe!"

"I think so." Kunya nodded. "A scout has ridden here with news for Mangas. Maybe he has seen a wagon train."

"Maybe there will be Mexican soldiers!"

"There will be a battle, maybe!"

Gokliya could not sleep. He polished his bow and sharpened his hunting knife again and again. He wished that he dared to put on war paint. But he was not a warrior yet. He knew that the others would laugh at that.

When the braves mounted their ponies at dawn, Gokliya was sure that this would be more than a hunt. Their faces and bodies were streaked with red, orange, and black. Each breechcloth, tied at the waist, dropped like an apron at front and back. Each warrior wore knee-high moccasins with long turned-up toes. They wore red headbands, and nothing else.

Mangas led them out through the pass. They rode down a twisting, narrow trail that circled through cactus-studded foothills. This trail led to the desert.

Mangas sent his scouts galloping away. Two rode far ahead of the column of warriors. Others rode out of sight to the left and right.

All day the trail led them sharply downward. They made camp close to the flat desert, near a road that bent around the foot of these mountains.

There were no campfires. Ah-Nay and three young braves led the ponies a little way up a sandy wash. They would guard them all night. Gokliya and Kunya climbed to the rim of a high mesa. Nolgee stood guard with them.

At first there was only the light of the stars but soon a great yellow moon slid into sight above the eastern mountains. Now they could see for miles.

Gokliya and Kunya whispered together about what might happen tomorrow. They did not dare to speak to Nolgee. Boys on their first hunts did not speak to warriors.

"Kunya," whispered Gokliya, "suppose a rich wagon train and many soldiers should ride toward us. Where would you place the warriors if you were chief?"

He did not wait for Kunya's answer. His words tumbled out. "I would place them there—and there—among those rocks. I would place them there, where the road bends. Others I would send through the hills to attack from the rear."

He was not whispering now. His voice rose with his excitement. Nolgee's sharp voice broke in. "Words, words, words! Gokliya's tongue is like an old grandmother's!"

Gokliya was ashamed and bit his lips. He would not forget again. After a little while Nolgee's voice came again. It was not angry now.

"That was a good plan for battle, Gokliya. You have learned your lessons well. Now be silent and keep watch."

The Indians broke camp long before sunrise. They had been on the trail just an hour when a scout raced up to Mangas. He jerked his pony to a

*He jerked his pony to a halt*

clattering halt that left its forelegs pawing high. He pointed toward the east.

"Many wagons! Many soldiers guard them!"

Mangas and the braves slid from their ponies. In a moment they had vanished among the boulders and clumps of cactus. At a word from Nolgee, the boys drove all the ponies into an arroyo between the foothills.

"Gokliya! Ah-Nay! Kunya!" Nolgee's voice was sharp. "Do not move from this spot! Stay with the ponies." He turned and ran back toward the trail on noiseless moccasins.

"Our first battle," said Ah-Nay, "and we won't even see it!"

"Our task is important," said Kunya. "We must not let the ponies get excited and run away."

"Don't talk," said Gokliya; "listen! Maybe we can hear the battle."

The boys heard the wind singing through the spines of the big cacti. They heard a woodpecker hammering at the spiny side of a giant saguaro. Except for that, the desert was still.

"They are waiting for the soldiers to ride into the ambush," whispered Ah-Nay.

Suddenly, a wild Apache war whoop rang out. It was followed by frightened cries and shouted commands in Spanish. Then the boys heard the screams of mules and plunging, rearing horses. They knew that Apache arrows were raining on the wagons.

Then came the crack of rifles. The firing was ragged as the soldiers searched the rocks for targets. Bullets whined and spattered against the boulders. All the while, shrill war cries filled the canyon. Soon the firing slackened. The yelling was farther away.

"The soldiers are retreating!" Gokliya shouted.

The boys waited, excited and miserable. "It will be a great victory and we missed it!"

There was a sudden sound behind them. A leather boot had kicked a stone. Gokliya whirled. Three Mexican soldiers had circled the hills. They were creeping now toward the Apache ponies.

Gokliya gripped Ah-Nay's arm and pointed. Ah-Nay and Kunya had seen the soldiers, too. They slipped behind a boulder, fitting arrows to their bowstrings.

Gokliya's bow and arrows lay a dozen feet away. He had only the hunting knife that he carried in his waistband. He stepped straight toward the soldiers. "If I can keep their eyes on me," he thought, "Ah-Nay and Kunya will have good targets for their arrows."

The soldiers saw that the Indian boys had discovered them. They sprang toward the horses, waving their arms and shouting to stampede them.

*The Indians were waiting among the rocks*

Gokliya heard the twang of two snapping bowstrings. Two arrows sang past his head. One buried its tip in a soldier's thigh. The other found a shoulder. Two soldiers screamed and ran.

The third soldier dropped to one knee. The round muzzle of his rifle was steady on Gokliya.

Gokliya sprang, dodging. The rifle barked. Gokliya felt a sharp tug at his hair. The bullet clipped his scarlet headband. It fell unnoticed into the dust.

He dived at the crouching soldier. His knife flashed up, then down. The soldier fell face downward.

"Gokliya! Gokliya!" It was Kunya calling. "The horses are frightened. Help us!"

The horses were milling wildly. They whinnied and snorted through flaring nostrils. The boys stroked their noses and flanks, and gathered up the halters.

Gokliya's heart was racing. He had defeated his first enemy. When the horses were quiet, he turned back to the spot where the soldier had fallen. He was gone! There were drops of blood on the rocks to mark his trail. Gokliya sprang after him. Then he remembered Nolgee's order—"Do not move from this spot." He turned back to guard the horses.

Soon the warriors came, laughing and chatter-

*The round muzzle was steady on Gokliya*

ing. Mangas nodded and smiled at the three excited boys. They mounted their ponies and rode with the braves to the captured wagon train. There were a dozen pack mules and eight huge wagons.

Nolgee rode beside Gokliya as Mangas led them up the trail toward the Apache village. "I am pleased with you, Gokliya," said Nolgee. "I saw the signs of your fight in the arroyo. You did well."

"Ah-Nay and Kunya did as much as I."

"You all did well. Mangas is pleased."

"Surely, Mangas had no time to notice us."

"There is little that Mangas does not notice," said Nolgee. "Now tell me all that happened."

Gokliya's excitement grew as he rode behind the warriors. They were near the Apache village. He saw the puffs of smoke on the peaks that told the people the warriors were coming. Now for the first time he rode with them through the pass and down to the waiting Indians. He helped to drive the captured mules toward the waving, cheering people.

There was feasting and dancing around the great campfires. The braves rose one by one and described the battle. Mangas spoke and praised each warrior. All had returned safely. There would be no burning wickiups tonight.

Mangas paused for a moment, and held his hand high. A long red cloth dangled from his hand. It was

Gokliya's red headband that the soldier had shot away.

"Gokliya! Ay-Nay! Kunya!"

The boys stepped into the firelight and stood beside their chief.

"These are no longer boys," said Mangas. "They were attacked by soldiers. The arrows of Ah-Nay and Kunya wounded two of the soldiers and drove them away. Gokliya's knife struck down another. These are no longer boys. They are warriors!"

Mangas flung his great arms around each one. The cheers of the people rang through the mountains. Gokliya saw his mother's face shining with pride. The three young Apaches smiled at each other and at the shouting people. They were men now—and warriors!

CHAPTER 5

# The White-Eyes

In 1846—the same year that Gokliya joined the council of warriors—the United States declared war on Mexico.

Gian-na-tah (Always Ready), chief of a tribe that lived near the Rio Grande, sent his scouts to Mangas with the news.

"There are many white soldiers," said the scouts, "and their nan-tan's name is Kearny. The Mexicans in the east have surrendered to Nan-tan Kearny at Santa Fé. Now the white men march this way."

Mangas was troubled by this news. He was not surprised to hear that the Mexicans had been defeated. He had nothing but scorn for them. But did the white soldiers come here only to fight Mexicans? Did they come to take this land for themselves? Was a new enemy marching against the Apaches? Mangas thought for a long time about these things.

He knew nothing at all about the United States. He had seen a few American traders and hunters. They carried long rifles and their eyes and hands were steady. They did not panic and run like Mexicans. These White-Eyes, these Pinda-Lick-O-Yi, came from somewhere toward the rising sun. Where and how they lived, Mangas did not know.

He called a council of his warriors and the wise men of the tribe. Mangas told them of the news from Gian-na-tah.

"I do not know why the white men fight the Mexicans. Maybe they will fight us, too. These things I do not know. We will not attack them, but we will watch them as they march."

He called to Nolgee and Gokliya. "Ride to meet the army of the White-Eyes. Do not let yourselves be seen. When you learn where they go, bring the news to me."

The two braves rode eastward through the mountains. After two days they climbed to a high lookout point to search the desert for signs of the white men. They saw a great cloud of dust hanging in the east. It moved slowly toward them. Such a dust cloud meant many riders.

Nolgee and Gokliya watched the dust cloud grow and come nearer. Finally, they saw the scouts of the marching column. Then came General Stephen

Kearny on his great horse. They counted scores of supply wagons and hundreds of mules.

"The White-Eyes are powerful," said Nolgee.

"We could defeat them," said Gokliya stoutly.

"Maybe they will be our allies. They have come to join us, maybe, in our war against the Mexicans."

"They are not our friends," said Gokliya. "They will make war against us. Delkey told me this long ago."

Nolgee and Gokliya followed the column of troopers all day. They camped that night where they could watch the campfires of the White-Eyes. On the second night, Kearny and his troopers halted at San Lucia Springs near the copper mines. No Mexican miners worked there now. The advancing Americans had frightened them away.

"Let us ride to Mangas," said Nolgee.

They found Mangas at his campfire in the Apache village. When he had heard the news they brought him, Mangas sat for a long time without speaking.

"Tomorrow," said Mangas, finally, "I will speak to Nan-tan Kearny. We will ride to his camp."

"There are many soldiers," said Gokliya. "Perhaps we should take all our warriors to show them that we are strong, too."

"No, we will go alone. We will take no warriors, no weapons." Mangas smiled at Gokliya's puzzled frown. "These white men may be friends—or they may be enemies. If they are friendly, we will offer them friendship. If they are enemies, it would be foolish to let them see how strong we are."

The next day, Mangas, Nolgee, and Gokliya rode to the American camp. Mangas smiled and made signs of peace. Gokliya's eyes were busy with the strange sights of an American army camp. He saw the straight rows of tents. He saw the stacked rifles and the picketed horses. And soldiers everywhere. Gokliya could not understand their words but he saw them jump to obey the orders of their chiefs. He glanced at Nolgee but he could not tell what Nolgee was thinking. Gokliya's face showed nothing but his heart was racing. He did not trust these men in the blue suits.

Troopers crowded around the Indians. They stared at the huge Mangas.

*"Buenos días,"* Mangas spoke in Spanish. "Where is the Nan-tan Kearny, your chief?" The soldiers laughed and shook their heads. They understood no Spanish.

Two men came up outside the ring of soldiers. The troopers made way for General Kearny. With him was a guide who spoke Spanish and Apache, too, and many other Indian tongues. He was Kit Carson.

General Kearny offered his hand. Mangas leaned down from his pony and put out his own brown hand.

"Tell him," said General Kearny to Kit Carson, "that we mean no harm to him or his people. Say that we have come to drive the Mexicans from New Mexico and Arizona. Then we will go on to California. These are the orders of the Great White Chief in Washington."

Mangas knew nothing of Washington or the Great White Chief. But he understood the rest. The White-Eyes would fight the Mexicans and then leave! Mangas leaped from his horse and shook hands again with General Kearny.

"*Enju! Enju!* Good! Good! The Mexicans are our enemies, too. We will help you in your war with them."

Carson sent a warning glance at General Kearny. "These are Apaches, General," he said in English. "I would not trust one of them."

"I don't," said Kearny, "but we do need some mules. Ask that big Indian if he can sell us some."

Mangas smiled and nodded. "We have many mules. My braves will round them up. Tomorrow we will bring them to Nan-tan Kearny."

The next day, Mangas and a few of the braves drove a dozen mules to the American camp. Kit Carson brought out some red-flannel shirts. He gave one to each Indian who had helped with the

mules. They were delighted with the bright color. He also gave Mangas a few silver coins.

"What are these?" asked Mangas.

"That is money," said Carson.

"What does one do with this money?"

Carson grinned. "Oh, let the youngsters play with it."

Mangas smiled. "These bright disks will please the children. They will have fine games with this money."

General Kearny and his men broke camp and

rode away toward the west. The Apaches galloped along beside the column of troopers, their red shirt-tails flapping in the breeze. The soldiers waved to the Indians. Soon the Apaches turned back toward their mountain camp.

Gokliya had rounded up no mules for the Americans. He watched from a high mesa until the soldiers were out of sight. Then he joined Mangas and the others as they rode toward their village.

"The soldiers will return," said Gokliya.

"Perhaps," said Mangas.

"I believe that they will return," said Nolgee. "They will bring trouble to our people. I saw no friendship in their eyes."

"They say they mean no harm to us," said Gokliya. "I am not deceived. I do not believe their words. They will try to take our land from us."

Nolgee nodded. Mangas smiled at the two warriors. "Does Gokliya think that Mangas is deceived? Does Nolgee think that Mangas is a child who can be won with red cloth and bright toys?"

Mangas shook his great head. "Mangas is not fooled by the White-Eyes. I, too, looked for friendship in the eyes of Nan-tan Kearny. There was none."

"Then let us attack them now as they ride across the desert," said Gokliya. "We can strike them again and again. Then they will be afraid to return."

"Gokliya is brave," said Mangas, "but if he would be a leader of our people, he must have more than reckless courage. It would not be good for our people to fight the White-Eyes now.

"Listen!" said Mangas. "Today, the Americans fight our Mexican enemies. They fight our battles for us. Now we can drive every Mexican from the land of our fathers. Then, if we must, we can fight the White-Eyes. One enemy at a time, Gokliya."

## CHAPTER 6

# Lone Raider

Gokliya found that Mangas's words were wise. The Mexican soldiers were busy in their war with the United States. There was no one now to protect their mines and ranches in the Apache country. Mangas sent his warriors swarming down from their mountains to the attack.

The wild-riding braves might strike a ranch today and a village a hundred miles away tomorrow. They swept the desert almost clear of Mexicans.

Gokliya's fierce joy shone in his eyes. He was a veteran now of many raids. He loved to feel his pony's heaving sides between his knees. He loved the smell of its wet flanks. He thrilled to the pounding speed of the attack and to the wild war cries of yelling Indians.

But this would never satisfy Gokliya. "Gokliya wants to be a chief, not just a warrior." Ah-Nay's joking words of long ago were true. Gokliya would never be satisfied only to follow other leaders.

In an Apache band, anyone could lead if he could find others who would follow him. If he won victories, many warriors would join him. Someday, he might be chosen as a war chief. Gokliya saw a chance to make his start in this campaign against the Mexican settlements.

A few Mexican ranches held out stubbornly. One, near Tres Alamos had beaten off every Apache attack. Mexican cowboys shot at the attacking Indians from the doors and windows of the ranch house. Several warriors had not returned from raids at Tres Alamos.

Gokliya begged the youngest warriors to follow him in an attack on this ranch. "I have a plan," he told them, "that will defeat the Mexicans at Tres Alamos. We can take many horses and scalps, maybe."

The braves laughed at Gokliya. "We follow Mangas. We follow our chiefs and sub-chiefs. Nobody follows Gokliya."

"Then I will attack this ranch alone!"

The warriors turned away laughing.

Gokliya left the village and walked beside the little stream. He was beginning to regret his rash words when he heard running steps behind him. Ah-Nay and Kunya joined him.

"I remember the words of Delkey," said Kunya. "Someday, you will be a war chief. Ah-Nay and I will be your first followers. We will follow you now."

"But can we three, alone, attack this ranch?" said Ah-Nay.

"I believe we can," said Gokliya eagerly. "The others failed because they did not drive the cowboys from the ranch house. The cowboys stayed safely behind their walls and shot at our people. We will not make this mistake."

"How can we drive them out?"

"With fire," said Gokliya. And Ah-Nay and Kunya nodded.

"There is danger for us," Gokliya went on. "We are only three against many. You must decide—will you come with me?"

"Yes!"

At dawn the three young Apaches rode down the twisting trail. They reached a grassy valley near the ranch on the second night. When the moon rose, they could see many cattle in the broad fields. There were fine horses in the corrals.

The lamps went out in the ranch house. Apaches never liked to attack at night, so they waited through the long hours of darkness. They worked as they waited. They pulled dry grass and tied it in thick tufts around the shafts of their arrows.

When the first light came in the east, they crept toward the ranch. The morning air was cold. The rancher and his cowboys would be deep in their blankets.

They crouched in a ditch and struck a fire. Flaming arrows sped toward the ranch house. Some flashed through the windows. Others plunked into the roof and stood quivering as they blazed. They watched as yellow flames licked at eaves and curtains. The dawn breeze fanned the fire. The flames leaped and grew.

The rancher stumbled out, choking, and ran toward the well. Kunya's bowstring snapped, and the rancher tumbled into the grass and lay still. Mexican cowboys leaped out through the smoke that was pouring now from doors and windows. They could see nothing except their fallen master and the burning house.

"Apaches! Apaches!" they shouted, as they scattered and ran.

Ah-Nay raced to the corral. He leaped on a wiry pony and drove the others through the gate. Gokliya and Kunya rounded up the cattle in the nearest field. They drove the cattle and horses before them as they began the long ride back to the north.

"The people will make a fine feast for us," said

Kunya. "Many warriors will follow Gokliya now."

They looked back often but there was no dust cloud over the trail. "They are too frightened to chase us." Ah-Nay laughed.

Late in the afternoon, the trail led past the foot of a steep cliff. A volley of shots rang out. The sound seemed to come from every side. There were enemies in front and behind. Unseen enemies on the cliff sent heavy boulders tumbling into the pass.

"Ambush!" shouted Gokliya.

They leaped from their ponies and pressed themselves flat against the rock wall of the cliff. Shots splashed against the wall. Splinters of rock stung their faces. They could not stay there. They sprang away from the cliff and ran dodging between the crashing boulders.

Ah-Nay stumbled. He ran on for a step. Then he fell heavily and lay still. Gokliya ran back to his side as bullets kicked up puffs of dust. Ah-Nay did not move. A bullet stung Gokliya's shoulder as it nicked the skin. He ran on. He saw a tumbling boulder pin Kunya to the ground.

Gokliya leaped into a small side canyon. His heart was sick as he ran. Ah-Nay and Kunya—tears stung Gokliya's eyes. He ran along the canyon floor

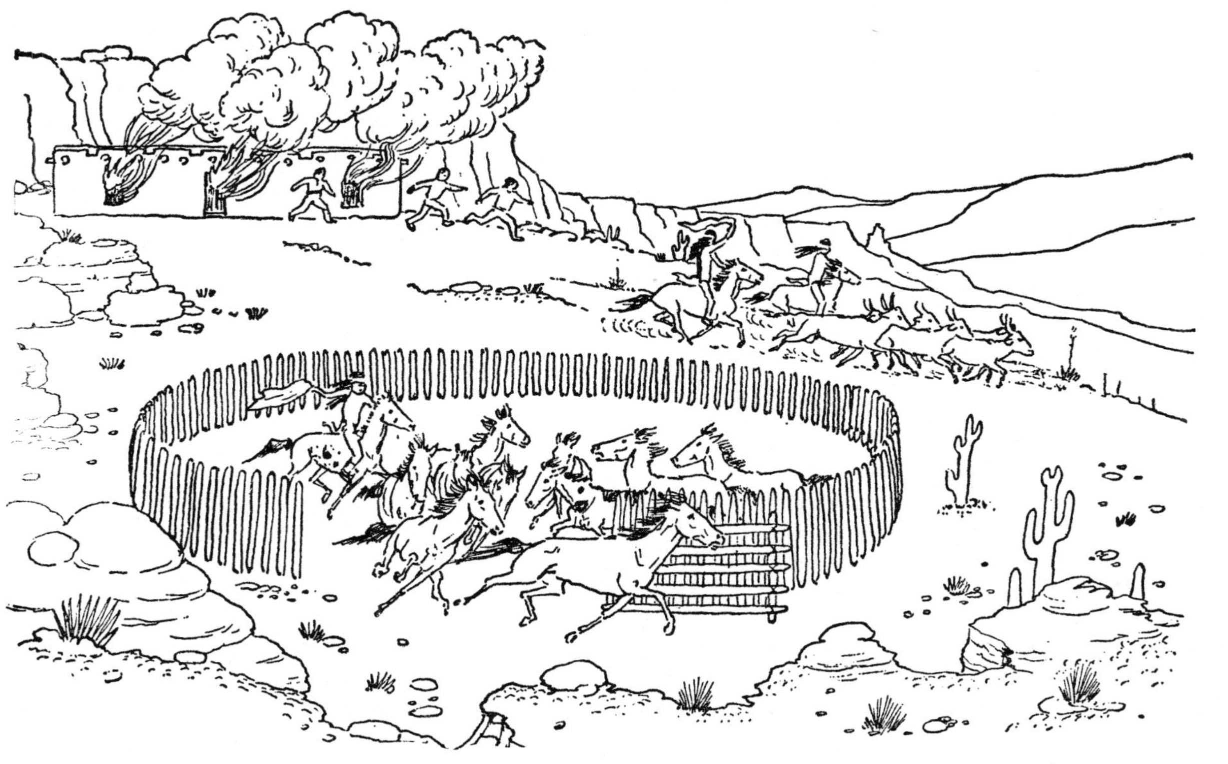

*He leaped onto a wiry pony and drove the others out*

as it twisted its way between the foothills. He left the canyon and climbed a rough hillside. There was a valley beyond. Gokliya fell into the tall grass and lay panting.

Gokliya blamed himself. "I was careless!" The cowboys had hurried to get help. They had circled through the mountains to set up an ambush for the Apaches.

He heard the cowboys calling to each other as they searched for him. They were in this valley now. They poked long rifle barrels into every bush. They walked slowly through the grass, so near that Gokliya held his breath. But the searchers moved on.

He lay still for an hour. Then he leaped to his feet and ran for cover into the hills that rose above this valley.

He found a muddy pool and dived into the water. Then he rolled in the mud at the side of the pool until his whole body was covered. Next he rolled over and over in the dry dust. Now he was just the color of the earth. He ran on.

He reached the Apache camp at sunset the next day. He was not running now. The bullet had left his shoulder sore and stiff. But he suffered more inside.

The people watched as he came with dragging

steps. They met him with many questions. "Where," they asked, "are Ah-Nay and Kunya?"

"They will not return," said Gokliya. He made no excuses and said nothing more. When an Apache leader won a victory, he told his story to the cheering people. When he failed, he took the blame and said nothing.

Gokliya sat alone that night on a hilltop and watched the flames as two wickiups were burned. Now the people turned away when Gokliya walked through the village. Even Alope, it seemed to Gokliya, seldom smiled at him now. He spent much time alone in the forest.

Mangas waited for him one day by the trailside. They sat together on the great trunk of a fallen pine tree.

"I know that your heart is heavy, Gokliya," said Mangas, "but you must mourn no longer. Your friends have died as many of us will die. Those who live must not turn their eyes to the past."

Mangas's quiet words were good.

"No leader lives who did not make mistakes," said Mangas. "You must learn from yours and not repeat them." He pressed Gokliya's arm and walked on toward the village. After a little while, Gokliya rose and followed. Now his chin was up and his step was quick and firm.

Next morning, Gokliya's mother hurried to Alope's wickiup.

"Gokliya did not return last night. Did he say to you where he was going?"

"No," said Alope. "Perhaps he is hunting in the hills. I have seen little of Gokliya. He spends much time alone."

There was no sign of Gokliya all that day or the next. Every morning, Alope ran along the mountain trails. She called his name but there was no answer from the forest. On the sixth day, there was a single puff of smoke from a lookout peak. One rider was coming toward the camp.

Soon the rider came through the pass. He rode a fine new pony. He was driving five horses before him. Each was loaded with a great canvas pack.

"It is Gokliya!" cried Alope.

He drove the horses to the waiting people. He leaped from his pony and swung down the heavy packs. He unrolled them on the ground.

The people ran up to see what he had brought. Apache braves squinted down the sights of many fine new rifles. They grunted their pleasure. There were cries of delight from the women when they saw the bright bolts of cloth, the tinware, and the sacks of meal and beans and coffee. The children shouted when Gokliya broke open packages of sugar.

There was much shouting of the name of Gokliya. His mother's face was bright with pride. Alope waved and smiled.

Gokliya had passed his greatest test. This booty that he had brought to his people proved many things to them. They knew now that Gokliya was fearless and that his body was strong. They knew that his mind was quick—that he could plan and carry out a raid. He proved that he thought first of his people by dividing his booty among them.

Apaches would never steal from each other. But they could see no wrong in an attack on any enemy or in taking what he had. No one, they thought, except Apaches had any right in this land that Usen had given them. Their greatest leaders were those who brought back the richest booty, who provided best for the needs of the tribe. To Apaches, only The People mattered.

They gave a great feast that night for the young warrior. They made him tell again and again of his adventure. He told how he followed the wagon train that brought supplies to the ranch at Tres Alamos—how he alone drove off the cowboys who guarded it—how two of them fell under his arrows.

"Ah-Nay and Kunya are avenged," he said.

Now Gokliya's long disgrace was over. The people no longer turned away when he passed by. The fiercest young braves would listen when he spoke. Many were eager to follow when he proposed a raid.

CHAPTER 7

# Alope

The Apaches ranged far across the desert on their raids. They climbed high into the mountains to hunt deer and wild turkeys. Sometimes, a few of them followed Gokliya. More often, all the warriors followed Mangas. As Gokliya rode with them to hunt or fight, his thoughts were often at home in the Apache village near the sparkling stream.

These were strange new thoughts to Gokliya. All his life his dreams had been of the warpath. Now, on the warpath, he dreamed of home. His heart beat fast whenever he rode through the narrow pass and saw the wickiups of his people. His eyes always searched among the waiting Indians for Alope. They searched until he saw her waving.

Gokliya's hand had never trembled in battle. But it trembled when he touched Alope's hand in the dances. When she smiled at Gokliya, he was warm inside. When she smiled at the other young braves, there was no sunshine in his heart.

Gokliya was sure that no one had guessed his thoughts. He never spoke of her to anyone. But his mother saw that Gokliya's eyes followed Alope when she walked to the stream to dip water. They were on her when she sat grinding corn meal near the door of her wickiup. Gokliya's mother smiled quietly to herself.

"Alope is now a beautiful young woman," she said.

Gokliya said nothing.

"She is slender and fair and her back is strong. Have you noticed, Gokliya?"

"Well," Gokliya stammered, "well—I suppose so."

"She will be a fine wife for some warrior. Perhaps one of the chiefs will want her. She smiles sometimes at Nolgee, too."

Gokliya's cheeks burned but he said nothing. He worked busily, polishing his great bow. His mother smiled at his bent head.

"Some warrior will offer Noposo, her father, many horses for Alope."

Gokliya leaped to his feet. His heart was hammering. "I—I must go now. I have much to do!"

His brain was whirling as he walked toward his

grazing ponies. Alope smiled at him, but she smiled also at others. Suppose some other brave should win Alope. Suppose one of the chiefs wanted her. It was very likely. There was no one else so fair in the whole Apache band. Or even in the whole tribe. Gokliya was sure of that.

His favorite pony nuzzled him. Gokliya stroked his neck. A fine horse was the greatest wealth an Apache could have. Any brave who had horses could afford a wickiup of his own.

Any brave who owned horses could find out just what an Apache girl meant when she smiled. Gokliya screwed up his courage. He would settle this doubt, once and for all. Then maybe he could think again of the important business of the warpath and the hunt.

He waited until the village was fast asleep. Then he took four of his best horses and tied them outside Alope's wickiup. He lay down behind a thick clump of bushes.

Gokliya knew that he would not sleep. Tomorrow, if Alope took the horses to drink from the stream, it would mean that her heart belonged only to Gokliya. If she left the horses tied, pretending not to see them, it would mean that Gokliya was not in her heart.

Somehow, the long night passed. As the sun came

up, it seemed to Gokliya that he could not wait another minute. He moved the thick bush and stole a quick look at Alope's wickiup.

Her father appeared, yawning and stretching. Noposo saw Gokliya's horses. He examined each one

carefully. He looked into their mouths and ran his hand over their lean flanks. He felt their strong legs. He nodded and walked on down to the stream to water his own string of ponies. Gokliya breathed a little easier. Noposo was satisfied with the horses he offered. Now, if Alope would only appear.

Her mother came out next to gather wood for her fire. There was no sign of Alope.

The sun moved higher and still Alope did not appear. The delay was not a bad sign. A modest Apache girl would wait for several hours. She would seem too eager if she hurried out in the early morning. She might wait all day. If she were a little cruel, she might wait through another night. She might even wait through four nights.

Gokliya understood that. Still, it did not make the waiting easier.

The sun was overhead when Alope appeared in the door of her wickiup. She knew that Gokliya was hidden somewhere nearby. She did not look for him. Her eyes were on the ground, but her lips were smiling. Gokliya's pulse raced. This was the moment. Would she pass by as if the horses were not there?

Alope walked straight to the horses. She stroked each one gently. She took their halters and led them toward the stream.

Gokliya's knees were weak. He wondered if they would carry him. He wanted to shout with joy but there was a huge lump in his throat. He forced himself to walk slowly toward Alope.

She turned shining eyes to the young Apache brave. She put out a slim brown hand. "Gokliya!"

Gokliya swallowed hard. Not a word would come.

Alope stroked a pony's nose. "Maybe you would

have me more modest. Perhaps I came out too soon."

"No," said Gokliya. His voice was husky. "No!"

Alope leaned close. "I have a secret, Gokliya. I should not confess it, maybe, but I wanted to run out as soon as it was light. Now you know all that is in my heart."

They were laughing together now. Gokliya pulled Alope gently away. The horses were forgotten. They walked up the hill to the edge of the forest. Gokliya looked down to see if it was the solid ground he walked on, and not a cloud.

They had played together in this forest many times when they were children. The thick pine needles had never been so fragrant before. The clouds had never been so white above the peaks. The birds had never sung as they were singing now.

Gokliya cut strong slim poles for their new wickiup. Alope decorated its buckskin walls with beads. She drew pictures of antelope, deer, and horses on the walls and dug the fire hole in the floor for warmth in winter.

They built their wickiup as far away as they could from Alope's mother. Gokliya must never speak to his mother-in-law. He must never even look at her. This was a rule of etiquette that all Apaches obeyed.

When Alope's mother came to visit her, Gokliya would run behind his wickiup to avoid her. He would stay in the forest until Alope called and said that she had gone.

Gokliya was often away on raids and hunts. It was good to ride with Mangas and the warriors. It was always good to come home to the welcome of Alope's smile.

CHAPTER 8

# "This Is Our War"

Gokliya sat in the sun near the door of his wickiup. He could hear Alope singing at her work inside. There was a great new bow on his knees. He fitted strips of deer sinew along its curving back.

He turned to look as a clatter of hoofbeats came from the trail. Nolgee slid from his horse and walked toward Gokliya.

"I have news for Mangas," said Nolgee.

"Mangas hunts in the northern canyons with some of the braves. He will return by nightfall." Gokliya looked curiously at Nolgee, who seemed puzzled. "What is this news?"

"There are many Americans camping in the desert," said Nolgee.

The bow slipped from Gokliya's knees. "Are they soldiers?"

"Some are soldiers but many are not. The soldiers carry weapons. The others carry strange tools that I have never seen before."

"Describe these tools," urged Gokliya.

"The Americans are scattered far across the desert," said Nolgee. "Some have look-far-away glasses which stand upon three legs. They look into these glasses. Then they shout to each other and wave their arms. Then other Americans make lines on paper. They seem to be peaceful, but I do not know what they are doing."

"Let us ride to the American camp. We can find out what they do, maybe, and tell Mangas when he comes."

They found the Americans working as Nolgee had said. Puzzled Indians were standing nearby and watching them. As Gokliya and Nolgee rode into the camp, one of the white men motioned to an Apache. The Indian shook his head. The American smiled and motioned again. Now the Indian stepped up and put his eye to the little telescope that stood on three thin legs. Then he turned away, laughing. The white men laughed, too, and invited other Indians to look into the telescopes.

Gokliya walked over to join them. He was curious and uneasy. He watched the soldiers closely. They seemed to be peaceful. They were laughing with the others. One of the white men nodded to Gokliya.

"Are you the nan-tan of these white men?" asked Gokliya.

The American called an interpreter and spoke to Gokliya.

"I am John Bartlett. Our President in Washington has sent me to find the new line that separates the United States and Mexico——"

"Do you still fight the Mexicans?" asked Gokliya.

"Oh, no," said Bartlett. "The war is over."

Gokliya had seen no Mexican soldiers here for a long time. But he knew nothing of the treaty of Guadalupe Hidalgo.

"Under this treaty of peace," said John Bartlett, "our flag will fly over New Mexico and Arizona. But we must know exactly where our country ends and Mexico begins. We will mark that line on a map."

"And have you found this line?" asked Gokliya.

Bartlett nodded. "The new boundary crosses that mesa. Then it dips into the desert and runs close to where we stand. It runs westward across that range of mountains."

Gokliya stared at the desert where Bartlett pointed. "I see no line. Perhaps you can see it when you look through the glass."

Bartlett smiled and shook his head. He invited Gokliya to look into his telescope.

Gokliya stooped and squinted. He could see the far-away top of the mesa where Bartlett said there was a line. He could see each leaf on bushes that grew a mile away. But he could see no line on the desert.

Bartlett took a large sheet of paper and walked a few steps away. He spread his feet wide apart and stood facing the east.

"My right foot is in Mexico. My left foot is in the United States. The country to the south belongs to the people of Mexico. The country to the north belongs to the people of the United States."

He showed the paper to the Indians. Gokliya stared at it, stony-faced.

"We draw the new border line on a map like this," Bartlett said. "No one may cross that line except in peace. Mexicans may not cross it to fight Apaches or Americans. Apaches may not cross it to fight Mexicans. This is written in the treaty of peace."

Now Gokliya's face was stormy. He swung his arm toward the south.

"The Mexicans do not own this land!"

He pointed to the northern mountains.

"That is not the land of the Americans!"

He snatched the map from Bartlett's hand. "All —all is the land of the Apaches! Usen gave it to my

*Gokliya stooped and squinted*

people. He marked no lines upon it for Mexicans and White-Eyes!"

Gokliya tore the map in two. "Thus I would destroy the treaty you have written. You can make no treaty for Apaches! No paper will stop our warriors. We fight the Mexicans wherever they are—in the north or in the south. This is our war!"

The other Indians edged nervously away as Gokliya's angry words exploded. Only Nolgee waited. Now Gokliya whirled to his pony. The two warriors galloped toward the mountains.

When Mangas rode in from his hunt, they told him of the Americans and their map.

"They divide our land between them. Some they give to the Mexicans. The rest is claimed by the White-Eyes. None is left for us. Do they think we will vanish from the earth?"

There was a clatter of hoofs as Delgadito, a subchief, rode into the village with ten of his braves. Delgadito leaped from his pony. Gokliya could see that he was angry. But he was puzzled, too.

"We attacked a Mexican ranch and took three prisoners," said Delgadito. "As we were coming here, we passed the American camp. The Mexicans called out to the Americans. At once, soldiers with rifles surrounded us and took our prisoners from us."

Delgadito took a deep breath. "The Americans set our prisoners free. They say we must not fight the Mexicans any more. We must not take prisoners from Mexican ranches. Nan-tan Bartlett says that the White Chief has made a treaty of peace for Apaches and Mexicans. Who is this White Chief? How can he do this?"

Mangas shook his head. He could not answer. Next morning he rode to the American camp and talked for a long time with John Bartlett. Mangas understood little of what Bartlett said. He did not see why Americans should draw maps to protect Mexicans.

"The Great White Father in Washington," said Bartlett, "protects all his children. He will protect Apaches, too."

"We protect ourselves," said Mangas proudly. "Let the Mexicans protect themselves."

He rode back to the Apache camp, still puzzled.

"Let us attack these Americans at once," urged Gokliya.

Mangas shook his head. "The Americans at Nan-tan Bartlett's camp are peaceful. They will soon be gone. He has told me that his work is almost done. Perhaps no other Americans will come."

That night, Delgadito came to Gokliya's wickiup. "Nan-tan Bartlett has many horses and mules," said Delgadito. "He takes our prisoners. Let us take his horses."

Gokliya smiled. "We will take them all. We will leave the Americans on foot in the desert."

Every night, Delgadito and Gokliya led a few

braves to the American camp. Every morning, Bartlett found that two or three, or a half dozen, of his horses and mules were gone. He placed double guards around the camp. The Apaches slipped by them like shadows.

Bartlett did not try to punish the raiding Apaches. He was not there to fight Indians. His job was to survey the border. He drove his men to finish their work quickly. In four months he was ready to leave.

The Apaches had taken 200 of his horses and

mules. Many of Bartlett's men had to walk as they left their desert camp. They left behind great piles of food, clothing, and blankets.

Gokliya and Delgadito laughed together at the campfire. "Let more White-Eyes come to make lines on paper if they leave such fine things for us."

Mangas was pleased. He did not ask too many questions about the new horses that grazed in the tall grass near the village. He was glad that there had been no battle and that no lives of his people had been lost.

CHAPTER 9

# Gold

The United States made peace with Mexico in 1848. In that same year, James Marshall was building a sawmill near Coloma on the banks of California's American River. He found a yellow flake in the gravel of the millrace. There was another—and another! He hurried to the office of his employer, John A. Sutter. They tested the yellow metal.

"Gold!"

The magic word—Gold!—flashed across the United States. Men sold their homes and everything they owned. They bought great wagons and set out for the West. Many of them came by the southern way—through the new border territory of New Mexico and Arizona. They came in a human flood. When the flood was at its peak, 50,000 people poured across Arizona in a few short months.

Most of the travelers hurried through the Apache country. They rode on to California as fast as straining mules could take them. But some of them liked the wide desert spaces of Arizona. They settled down to raise cattle in the Santa Cruz, Sonoita, and San Simon valleys. Many others failed to get rich quickly in California. They wandered back to search for gold in the rugged mountains of New Mexico and Arizona.

They found a rich vein of gold at Santa Rita—close to the spot where the Mexicans had worked their copper mines. Now white men swarmed into the foothills and canyons around Santa Rita.

They came on in spite of the Apache danger. They dreamed of gold, and if Indians were in the way, the Indians would be pushed aside. Many an Apache was shot on sight. Many a prospector was ambushed and killed.

Mangas tried to keep the peace. He called a council of his Warm Springs warriors.

"I do not know why the white men prize this yellow iron," said Mangas. "It cannot be eaten. It is too soft for weapons. Yet the Americans will kill to get it."

The warriors nodded. "I do not wish war with these Americans," Mangas went on. "Perhaps when they have dug all the yellow iron they will leave our country."

Most of the sub-chiefs agreed with Mangas. Then Gokliya spoke.

"We should have killed the first white man who came to this land that Usen gave us. And the second —and all the others. Then these men would have been afraid to come. Let us go to war now against these diggers of the yellow iron. Otherwise. so many will come that we cannot defeat them."

There was a murmur from the young warriors who followed the fiery Gokliya. *"Enju! Enju!* Gokliya speaks wisely."

But Mangas rose again. "Gokliya may be right, but first I will try a plan that has come to me. It is better to win battles without bloodshed. If my plan is good, the miners will go away of their own will.

"We know that there is yellow iron in the Mother Mountains of the south. There is more, much more than at Santa Rita. I have seen it." Mangas turned to Delgadito, who nodded in agreement. "Delgadito has seen it, too.

"This is my plan. I will go to the camp of the miners and tell them of this gold in the Mother Mountains. I will guide them there. When they have seen it, they will be glad to leave Santa Rita."

"They will not believe you," said Gokliya.

"I will speak only the truth. They will see that my tongue is straight."

"Let the warriors come with you," said Delgadito.

"No," said Mangas, "if I go alone, they will understand that I come in peace."

Delgadito was worried as Mangas rode away. He spoke quietly to Gokliya. "Let us follow Mangas through the hills. We can watch from the rocks above the camp."

The two Apaches galloped toward Santa Rita. They crept up a rocky hillside. From its top they saw Mangas ride into the camp. They saw his smile and his sign of friendship.

Mangas spoke to the miners in Spanish. One or two of them could understand. They translated his words for the others. "My people wish to be friendly," said Mangas. "As proof of this, I have come to tell you where there is much gold."

He pointed toward the south. He told them of the gold he had seen in the Sierra Madre. "I will guide you to this place. I will show you this gold."

The miners laughed and shouted to each other, "Come hear this fairy tale!"

Mangas did not understand what they said to each other. He went on speaking. "It is not far—a few days' journey. . . ."

"Listen to the old liar!"

"He wants to lead us into the desert and then kill us all!"

"Wait a minute," said one miner. "Maybe he's

*They saw Mangas ride into camp*

telling the truth. Maybe there is more gold where he says."

"We can't take a chance on that!" shouted another. "All of these Apaches are killers. We've got to think of our families."

Another wagged his head wisely. "It's a trick, that's what it is. I know these Apache tricks."

"Let's teach this heathen a lesson," roared a big, brown-bearded miner. "Drag him off that horse!"

Many arms reached up and pulled Mangas from his pony. He fought like a mountain lion but they wrestled him to the ground. They tied his arms with rope. Then they tied his wrists to the low branches of a tree. His toes just touched the ground as he swung helplessly.

Brown-beard ran up with a long blacksnake whip. It whistled across the back of the Apache chieftain. The miners counted the blows in a laughing chant.

"One . . . two . . . three . . . four. . . ."

Mangas did not make a sound. His face did not change but his eyes blazed at the circle of men. The great muscles of his back quivered as the whip left bloody stripes.

"Fifty-one . . . fifty-two. . . ."

Gokliya and Delgadito burned with helpless rage. Gokliya would have plunged down the hillside into the ring of laughing miners. Delgadito gripped his arm. "Wait. We cannot help Mangas now. Wait."

"Ninety-eight . . . ninety-nine . . . one hundred!"

The miners cut Mangas down. "That'll teach you to try your Indian tricks on us!"

Mangas pushed his way through the crowd of men. He walked steadily until he was out of sight. Then he sank to the ground.

Gokliya and Delgadito raced to his side and helped him to mount Gokliya's pony. They led him to a secret hide-out far from the Apache camp. Mangas stayed in hiding until his back had healed. Then Gokliya brought him a shirt to hide the scars.

"We will not speak to anyone of my shame," said Mangas, "but I will not live long enough to forget it.

"Ride, Gokliya, to the camps of our people. Delgadito, make smoke on the mountain peaks. Say that Mangas takes the warpath and fights to the death against the White-Eyes!"

CHAPTER 10

# Apache Vengeance

The Warm Springs Apaches gathered in Mangas's camp. The news that Mangas took the warpath quickly reached the other Apache tribes. From the east came scores of Mescalero Apaches. Cochise, chief of the Chiricahua Apaches, sent forty braves. Fighting men came from other tribes—the Tontos, the White Mountains, the Pinals.

The warriors listened in wonder to Mangas's words. Even Apaches had never seen a man so full of quiet, deadly rage.

"I have tried to live at peace with the White-Eyes. You know it." Mangas's eyes swept the war-painted faces. "I was wrong. There can be no peace between Apaches and Americans. They cannot live in the same land together. One must go and one must stay. One must live and one must die. Which shall die—Apaches or Americans?"

"Death to the White-Eyes!"

The buckskin drums rolled out the beat of the war chants.

*"Enju!"* said the grim-faced Mangas. *"Enju!"*

He called Gokliya, Nolgee, and Delgadito to his side.

"Supplies come to the miners at Santa Rita by many trails. If no wagons reach these miners, they will soon have no food. Then they will go into the hills to hunt. Or they will ride to the American towns to seek food. Not a hunter, not a rider will return. See to this, Gokliya—Nolgee—Delgadito."

Nolgee rode out of the mountains with twenty braves. He ambushed a supply train that was bound for Santa Rita. It was guarded by seven riders. Nolgee left seven bodies on the desert. He drove thirty mules, with their heavy packs, to Mangas's camp.

Gokliya, with fifty warriors, cut the trails that led to Santa Rita from the west and south. Not a rider passed him. Not a wagon got through to the miners.

Mangas and Delgadito ranged through the hills above the mines. Apache eyes watched every movement in the miners' camp. If one of them wandered into the hills, a brown body dived from a high boulder and crashed upon his back. An Apache knife flashed, and another miner vanished.

Soon there was growing panic at the mines. They

*A knife flashed and another miner vanished*

never saw an Apache but they could feel the watching eyes. No supply trains came. Food and ammunition were low. Each day the miners climbed on high rocks to look out across the desert. Nothing at all moved. They waited day after day for help that did not come.

One day, Mangas and Delgadito saw a great stir in the camp. Fourteen miners mounted the best horses. Another drove an empty wagon. Cheered by the miners in the camp, they set out for the south.

"They ride for help and food," said Delgadito.

"They ride toward Gokliya," said Mangas. "Make smoke to warn him."

Delgadito built a small fire, using green sticks that would smoke freely. First, he let a long, thin column of smoke rise steadily from the tall peak. This was a call to attention. Delgadito covered the fire for a moment with his blanket. Then he whipped the blanket away, letting a short, round puff of smoke roll upward. He did this again and again. Puff after puff of smoke rose and vanished quickly in the thin, high air. This was a warning that heavily armed enemies were coming.

Delgadito repeated his signal and then stamped out the fire. Then he rode with Mangas through the hills to join Gokliya.

A few miles away, Gokliya saw the smoke. Soon

he could see the cloud of dust raised by the riders and their wagon. He quickly hid his warriors where the trail ran between high boulders. They lay flat on the great rocks.

The miners halted where the trail narrowed to pass the boulders. A scout rode ahead into the pass. The Apaches made no sound as he rode by close beneath them. The scout's eyes searched the trail. He turned and waved the miners forward.

The horses struck sparks from the rocks as their riders spurred them through the dangerous pass. The wagon driver whipped his plunging mules. The empty wagon clattered on the loose stones. Now they were just below the waiting Indians.

"Death to the White-Eyes!"

Gokliya dived from his rock. He dropped astride the leading rider's horse. His brown arm circled the startled miner's throat. His knife gleamed in the sun for an instant. The miner slumped to the ground. Gokliya snatched up the reins and whirled to join the battle.

At Gokliya's shout, the other Indians had leaped from their rocks. They grappled and fought with the riders. Four Apaches dropped into the flat bed of the wagon. Their knives flashed and the driver toppled slowly from his high seat. An Indian pulled the frightened mules to a halt.

On the ground, an Apache sat on a struggling miner. One hand grasped the miner's hair. The other raised a knife.

Gokliya recognized that big, brown-bearded white man. He kicked the flanks of his captured horse and galloped toward the struggling pair. He leaped to the ground and twisted the Apache's knife from his hand. The puzzled Indian looked up at his leader.

"Do not kill this one," said Gokliya.

The fight was over now. Eight miners lay in the trail. Two lay at the bottom of a steep cliff just off the roadway. Five others were alive and unhurt.

"Remember," said Gokliya, pointing to the man he had saved, "I want no harm to come to this man. He belongs to Mangas."

He strode up to the other four. His knife flicked off their buttons. Many hands helped him to rip off their clothing.

"There is a fine clump of cactus." He pointed to a thick, knee-high forest of Teddy-bear cholla that grew on a slope below the trail. This was the dreaded jumping cactus, hated and feared by every desert man and beast. Its spines looked soft and silvery. No pricklier plant ever lived.

The Apaches whooped with laughter. They

seized two of the miners by heels and hands. They swung them back and forth—then tossed them into the center of the patch of cactus.

Mangas and Delgadito galloped up, their ponies blowing foam. When they saw that the fight was over, they sat and watched the busy Indians.

Gokliya gave a sharp command. Two miners were grabbed and bound, with arms and legs spread wide, to the wheels of their wagon. The Indians unhitched the mules. They piled dry grass into the wagon's bed and set it afire. When it was blazing freely, they pushed the wagon to the edge of the cliff and rolled it over.

The wagon quickly gathered speed. The wheels turned faster. Faster spun the miners bound to the spokes. The wagon crashed into the boulders at the bottom of the cliff. A great spray of sparks and flames roared upward.

Gokliya turned to Brown-beard, the last miner. He flung him sprawling at the feet of Mangas's pony.

"Do you know this man?"

Mangas's eyes blazed. He had last seen Brown-beard when he held a blacksnake whip. Mangas's back would bear its scars forever.

"I have saved his life for you," said Gokliya. "What will you do with him?"

*They tossed the miners into a patch of cactus*

"Was there no whip in the wagon?" asked Mangas.

Gokliya nodded. A brave ran up with the whip.

"Perhaps a hundred blows of the whip?" asked Gokliya.

Mangas watched, stony-faced, as the whip whistled and struck. But soon he stopped the whipping.

"Let him go," said Mangas. "The man is weak. I do not want him to die. Let those in the cactus go with him. Let them go back to the mines and tell of their adventures."

CHAPTER II

# Massacre

Between their raids on the mines and ranches of the White-Eyes, Mangas's braves ranged far into the mountains, hunting fresh meat for the people. They killed deer and bears and antelope. They trapped beaver and hunted buffalo. They had great piles of skins and hides.

There was little trouble now with the Mexicans. They stayed on their own side of the line that John Bartlett had drawn upon his map. When things were peaceful between Apaches and Mexicans, the Indians sometimes traded their skins and hides in the Mexican town of Casas Grandes. Now they left their winter camp for another trading journey.

Mangas led the band of eighty warriors. The women and children went along. The old men and the wounded warriors rode with them. Juana was with Gokliya and Alope and their three small children. It was like a vacation trip for the whole Apache band.

The spring sun was warm on the desert. The great blossoms of the cacti splashed color across the foothills. The palo verde trees were lacy with golden blossoms. Millions of bees hummed in the desert flowers.

The Indians were on the trail for many days. There was no hurry. They danced and sang in their camps at night. The women cooked and gossiped. Children explored the canyons and foothills.

They never knew when they crossed the border—that line on the sand that Apache eyes could not see. Scouts from a Mexican fort saw them come into Mexico and followed them as they rode.

The scouts counted the Indians and then galloped off to the fort at Janos with the news. Here were lots of Indians! And their government still offered one hundred dollars for the scalp of any Apache man. They would pay fifty dollars for an Apache woman's scalp, or twenty-five dollars for a child's.

The Apaches camped near Casas Grandes. Mexican soldiers surrounded the camp in the darkness.

Next morning, the braves piled the hides on their

mules and led them into the town. The women would come later to choose bright cloth, beads, and tinkling silver ornaments in exchange.

The soldiers waited until the warriors had disappeared. Then they charged through the Indian camp with bayonets fixed. They worked with breathless speed. They attacked the old men and the wounded warriors. Then they turned their knives and bayonets on the others. Not a shot was fired to warn the warriors in the town.

The Apache braves came back late in the afternoon. They were stunned for a moment at their first sight of the camp. Then their voices rose in long wails of helpless rage. They ran through the camp and then raced across the foothills searching for their enemies. The soldiers had gone.

Gokliya's voice was silent. He walked slowly through the ruined camp. He found his people. The children, his mother and Alope—there was nothing he could do for them. Finally, he walked alone into the twilight. There was a burning rage in his heart now that never would go out.

When it was dark, the warriors crowded around Mangas. Gokliya took his place in the council of warriors. Mangas's voice was quiet.

"We cannot take our revenge now. Our ponies and most of our weapons are gone. We are far from home. First, we must escape with our own lives. Let us go home with all the speed we can."

Gokliya did not walk with the others. He could hear their soft moccasins just ahead but he did not try to overtake them. He did not want to talk.

After a long time, Nolgee waited for Gokliya beside the trail. They walked together without speaking.

"There is nothing to say," Gokliya whispered, finally.

"We will speak with our weapons," said Nolgee. "Soon—soon we will speak with our weapons!"

The Apaches reached their mountain camp. That night, Gokliya burned his wickiup. The flames from many other wickiups rose blazing into the night and then burned low. They shone on the grim faces of many warriors.

Mangas called a council. "We return to Mexico. Ten lives—a hundred lives—shall pay for every life that we have lost!"

The war cries were the wildest these hills had ever heard. Mangas held up his hand for silence.

"We will ask our kinsmen of other tribes to join us on this warpath. Gokliya, ride to Cochise. Tell him that Mangas takes the warpath. Ask him to join us with his Chiricahua warriors."

Gokliya sprang to his pony. He was gone before

*They were stunned at the sight of their camp*

Mangas's words were finished. He sped westward toward the stronghold of Cochise. His pony seemed to feel already the excitement of the warpath. Gokliya kept him at a pounding gallop as the trail wound into the steep mountains.

Gokliya found the great Cochise in his high fortress. It was a rocky bowl thousands of feet above the desert floor.

Cochise called his warriors to hear Gokliya. They sat in rings on the ground to listen. Cochise stood nearest Gokliya. His sub-chiefs sat in a ring around them. Gokliya recognized Skinya and Pion-se-nay. These two brothers—Skinya small and slight; Pion-se-nay big, round and burly—bore names that were famous among all Apaches. The other warriors sat farther away. Farthest back of all, the youngest warriors sat on the steep hillsides. Gokliya spoke to hundreds of silent Indians.

Quietly he told them of the journey into Mexico and of the massacre of his people. He told of Mangas's plan for vengeance. Then his voice rose.

"Kinsmen!

"You are our people. You are our uncles—brothers—cousins. Join with us! Our warpath leads to Mexico. I will guide you to their city. I will fight in the front of the battle. Will you come?

"Do not mourn for me if I am killed. If your lives

are lost, I will not mourn for you. You could not lose them in a better cause. Let us ride this warpath together! Will you come?"

No Apache chief—not even Cochise—could take his braves to war against their will. He turned to his warriors to take the vote.

There was no time for voting. An angry murmur began among the Chiricahua Apaches. It swelled into a mighty roar of rage.

Cochise smiled at Gokliya. "As you see, my warriors will come. Say to Mangas that Cochise will join him."

CHAPTER 12

# Geronimo! Geronimo!

Cochise came with 200 warriors. Whoa, chief of the Mescalero Apaches, rode with his fiercest braves. Mangas and the Warm Springs bands welcomed their kinsmen to this warpath.

They left their ponies deep in a lonely canyon near the border. A few of the youngest braves were left behind to guard them. The warriors would march into Mexico on foot. Moccasins would make no noise on the trail.

The Indians carried nothing except their weapons. They wore moccasins and breechcloths. Headbands bound back their hair. Faces were streaked with orange, red, and black.

No scouts saw them now as they slipped southward through the canyons, over the foothills. On the fourth day, they crept down from the hills that overlooked the town. Below the hills was a ring of trees. Inside the trees, a small plain lay before the town.

The Apaches took cover among the trees. They could see into the dusty streets of the town. They saw soldiers in uniform and burros led by Mexicans in broad hats and bright serapes.

"Let a few of our warriors show themselves," said Mangas.

Six Apaches left the cover of the trees. They walked out into the grassy meadow and waved and shouted to the Mexicans.

A Mexican officer soon rode out, followed by seven soldiers. "What do you do here?" demanded the officer.

At a signal from Mangas, thirty Apaches sprang toward the soldiers. The Indians dragged them from their horses. Apache knives flashed. The Indians danced about their victims. Then they ran back to the trees and disappeared.

"That will bring the soldiers out upon the plain," said Cochise.

"Yes," said Mangas, "but it grows dark now. They will wait until the morning."

The Indians crept back into the foothills to camp for the night. When the moon had risen, a messenger came for Gokliya. He led the young warrior to the camp of the chiefs. There Gokliya found Mangas, Cochise, and Whoa resting in a little ravine.

"Many of us lost our loved ones here," said

Mangas, "but Gokliya's thirst for revenge is deepest. He has dreamed of this battle that we will fight tomorrow. Not for a moment has it been out of his thoughts. This I have seen in his eyes."

"His words brought my people eagerly to the warpath," said Cochise.

"Gokliya shall lead the warriors tomorrow," said Mangas. "The warriors of Cochise and Whoa shall follow him. This battle is Gokliya's."

Gokliya's heart swelled with pride. At last he would lead the braves in a great battle. He glanced at Cochise and Whoa. They nodded to show that they agreed with the words of Mangas.

"May it be well," said Whoa.

Cochise smiled at the eager Gokliya. If he felt any doubt about trusting his braves to this young warrior, he gave no sign of it.

At dawn, Gokliya stood on a high boulder. His arms were outstretched, his face lifted to the sky. He prayed to Usen, Great Spirit of the Apaches.

It was not the Apache way to pray for help in battle. Gokliya did not ask for help. He prayed only that his eyes might be sharp, so that enemy tricks would not deceive him. He asked Usen to keep his muscles strong for the long test of battle. For everything else, in victory or defeat, an Apache warrior would depend upon himself.

Gokliya placed his warriors among the trees. At each end of his line, commanded by Skinya and Pion-se-nay, were scores of archers and a few Indians who had rifles and knew how to use them. In the center, many other braves crouched with their twelve-foot lances.

Gokliya called to Nolgee. "Take fifty warriors. Circle these low hills and attack from the rear when the battle starts."

Suddenly, wild Apache yells told Gokliya that the soldiers were advancing. He leaped to a tall rock.

Two companies of infantry marched from the town. They formed a long line that stretched across the plain. They walked slowly toward the trees that hid the Apaches, their rifles ready. Their bayonets were bright in the early sun.

Two troops of horsemen trotted behind the infantry. They rode slowly, ready to charge into the thick of the fight when it started.

"Stampede the horses!" shouted Gokliya.

Skinya and Pion-se-nay rapped out orders to their bowmen. Arrows rained among the horsemen. Some horses fell and their riders tumbled to the grass. Others plunged forward through the line of advancing infantry.

"Follow me!" shouted Gokliya to the lancers.

Hundreds of yelling, war-painted braves surged from the trees. They leaped toward the line of soldiers. The Mexicans stood firm under the heavy charge. Their rifles crashed in Apache faces.

The Indians plunged on, stabbing and throwing their lances. Many grappled hand-to-hand with the soldiers. They rolled together on the ground. Flashing knives rose and fell.

Mexican horsemen rode among the twisting, wrestling bodies. They swung their sabers at the dodging Indians. Nolgee and his fifty warriors charged into the fight with shrill war cries. Some soldiers turned to meet this new danger from the rear. The Indians in front pressed forward.

The battle raged for two hours. The soldiers were slowly pushed backward. Many of the horsemen turned and raced off the battlefield, followed by clouds of arrows. Some of the infantry took cover behind fallen horses and kept up their fire.

The soldiers retreated from one corner of the field, leaving Gokliya alone with three warriors. But the Indians were unarmed. Their spears were broken and all their arrows were gone. Four soldiers saw the unarmed Indians and charged them with bayonets fixed. Their bullets cut down two of the braves. Another turned to run and was pinned to the ground by a bayonet.

*"Circle these hills and attack from the rear"*

Gokliya turned and sprinted toward the trees. The soldiers plunged after him.

But Gokliya ran only to the edge of the woods. There he searched frantically for a weapon, any weapon. He snatched up a long spear from the grass and whirled to face the soldiers. He ran at them headlong. His spear ran the first soldier through. Gokliya caught the soldier's saber as he fell. The whistling blade sent a second enemy sprawling.

Skinya and Pion-se-nay and their archers watched. A great cheer went up for Gokliya. Their war whoops rolled across the battlefield.

The last two soldiers turned to escape. Gokliya leaped on the back of one of them and bore him to the ground. He leaped up to chase the other.

The chase led Gokliya far across the battlefield where the fighting still raged. The fleeing soldier's comrades shouted to warn him that the plunging Apache was close behind.

*"Geronimo! Geronimo!"* was the Mexicans' warning cry.

The Apaches heard the cry. They jeered at the panicky soldiers and copied their cry of warning.

*"Geronimo! Geronimo!"* shouted the Indians.

With a great leap, Gokliya caught the terrified soldier. With quick slashes of his knife he struck him down. He plunged on, leaping over the bodies of fallen men and horses, diving headlong at the soldiers who were now in full retreat. His flashing knife was busy.

The strange new cry followed him everywhere.

*"Geronimo! Geronimo!"*

It became the battle cry of the Indians. But now the battle was almost over. There were a few more ragged shots from the defeated soldiers and then the battlefield was quiet.

That night, the Indians marched northward in triumph. Gokliya walked just behind the chiefs. They made camp by the trailside and killed captured mules for a feast of victory.

After the feasting, they sat around the campfires. Cochise and Whoa spoke and praised the warriors.

Gokliya sat silently. Nobody had mentioned his name.

Then Mangas rose and stretched out his hand to the young warrior. Gokliya stood beside his chief.

"This is no longer Gokliya," said Mangas. "Today our enemies have named him. He has won another name in battle. From this day, he is called Geronimo!"

The cheers of the warriors drowned Mangas's words.

"Geronimo! GERONIMO!"

Mangas motioned for silence and the cheering died.

"This is Geronimo—War Chief of the Apache Nation. This is Geronimo—War Chief of The People. Will you follow Geronimo in battle?"

The cheers were louder than ever. The young warrior stood motionless and looked with shining eyes at the yelling, dancing braves.

He was a war chief of the Apaches. He was one of the trusted leaders chosen to defend them. He had dreamed of this when he played as a child near his mother's wickiup. The dream had never left him.

It was well that the cheering was so loud and that the new war chief was not called upon to speak. His brain was whirling and there was a lump in his throat. He knew that he could not say a word.

CHAPTER 13

# Apache Victory

More than 5,000 white men lived in Arizona now. The Butterfield Stage Lines sent guarded coaches rumbling through Apache Pass. Mail riders galloped through the Apache country between the desert towns.

The government in Washington could give little thought to the Apache danger far away in the Southwest. Congress was busy with the arguments over slavery that split the North and the South. The black threat of Civil War hung over the United States.

A few soldiers were sent to the desert country. They were ordered to drive the Apaches from the warpath and force them to live in peace. They were to change Apaches overnight from free-roving hunters and fighters to peaceful villagers. It simply could not be done.

Some of the Army's officers saw the problem

clearly. Even if Apaches should agree to live in peace, the Apache problem would not be solved. They would need food, blankets, clothing, horses, cattle, the things they had always taken in their raids. Who would give them these things until they could learn to earn them for themselves in peaceful ways? Certainly not the white settlers in the Apache country. They poured scorn on any effort to persuade Apaches to be peaceful.

"Just make good Indians of them," they urged the officers, "and the only good Indian has a bullet in his heart."

Of course, the Apaches fought them all—settlers and soldiers alike. The mountain trails were dotted with burned-out stagecoaches and wagons. Spirals of smoke from burning ranches and villages showed where Apache raiders had struck. Many a mail rider vanished. The Superintendent of Mails at Tucson said that he hired lots of men but paid only a few salaries. "Not many of them are alive at the end of the month to collect their pay."

The United States Army built forts in the Apache country to protect the settlers. They built Fort Buchanan in the Sonoita Valley. There was a garrison of troops at Tucson.

In April, 1861, when Geronimo was thirty-two years old, the guns at Fort Sumter in South Carolina fired the opening shots of the Civil War. The Apaches knew nothing of the war between North and South. But galloping messengers from the east brought orders to every desert fort. The soldiers could not be spared to fight Indians in the far Southwest. They were ordered to march eastward and join in the battles along the Potomac.

One day that summer, Cochise and Mangas stood on a lookout point high in the cool Chiricahua Mountains. Heat waves danced on the blistering desert below. They could see whirling wind-devils that sucked the hot sand up into tall thin funnels. Mirages made the distant mountains seem to stand in pools of water.

In the west they saw a great moving cloud of dust that hung over many riders. The Apache chiefs watched for hours as the dust cloud came nearer. Finally, they could see loaded wagons and the blue uniforms of the soldiers.

Cochise snapped an order to two of his braves. "Make smoke to bring all our warriors. The White-Eyes come to attack us in our mountains——"

Clattering hoofs cut his words short. Geronimo's heaving pony raced up the twisting trail to the lookout point. "The soldiers! The soldiers from Fort Buchanan!"

"We have seen them," said Mangas. "We are ready."

"They dare to ride against us here!" said Cochise.

"No!" said Geronimo. "They do not ride against us. They ride away to the east!"

Cochise and Mangas smiled. They did not believe it.

"The soldiers have left the forts," insisted Geronimo. "We have beaten the White-Eyes! We have driven their armies away!"

Cochise sent his scouts to trail the soldiers. They reported that the soldiers rode steadily eastward. They were joined by soldiers from other forts. All the forts were empty.

Cochise turned to Mangas. He swept his arms toward the deserts and mountains that Usen had created for the Apaches. "The Americans are defeated! This shall be our land again!"

There were wild victory dances in every Apache camp. Their yells of triumph rang through the mountains. That night, the hills were dotted with great fires as they prepared their feasts.

Next morning, Geronimo spoke to the warriors who followed him. "There is much fighting still to do. The soldiers are gone but there are white men in the towns. There are ranches and farms and mines."

Now with the soldiers gone, the Apaches rode boldly out of their mountain fortresses. They burned the ranches. They captured and looted whole villages. The ranchers and farmers left their homes and went to live in Tucson and Tubac to protect each other. They could not hold Tubac. They left that town to be destroyed by the Indians and crowded into Tucson.

The Apaches burned the empty forts. Except for the frightened people of Tucson, there were few white men alive in southern Arizona. Those in the town were never safe. The Apaches often rode close enough to fire their rifles and arrows into the streets. No one dared to go outside at night. He might be snatched away, almost from his doorstep, by galloping braves.

One day, Geronimo sat with Mangas on a peak above the village of their Warm Springs band. As far as Indian eyes could see across deserts, mesas, and mountains this was Apache land again.

There were hundreds of happy Indians in the valley below them. They watched the children running with their dogs between the wickiups and the women carrying water from the stream. War ponies grazed peacefully in the tall grass. Warriors lay in the sun.

"Thus it was when Usen gave this land to us,"

said Geronimo. "This will always be the land of our people."

Mangas did not answer. He had been sitting silently for a long time. His great shoulders were bent. Lines creased his forehead. He was deep in thought.

"A scout from our Mescalero kinsmen has

brought strange news to me," said Mangas, finally. "They heard this story from a captive white man, but they did not believe it. Then other captives said the same."

"What is this news?"

"It is said that the soldiers have left the forts to fight in another war far away in the east. Two tribes of white men fight each other. The soldiers were tribesmen of the North. They went to help their brothers."

"It is not true!" said Geronimo. "Our warriors drove them away. They left the forts because they were defeated!"

"It is said," Mangas went on, "that when the Americans make peace, they will join together to fight against us. More soldiers will come. More forts will be built."

"Look!" said Geronimo. He pointed toward the deserts that stretched away on every side. "There were many white invaders. Now there are none. They will not dare to return!"

Mangas shook his head. "I think this news is true," he said quietly. "I think that I have always known it. The Americans will return."

"Then we will drive them away again!"

"I have lived long," said Mangas. "I am no longer thirsty for warfare and revenge. Perhaps I am wiser now. This I think is true—someday, we must learn to walk in peace with white men. Many Americans will come—so many that we cannot defeat them. We must find a way to live peacefully together."

He turned away and walked down toward the village. The puzzled Geronimo watched him go.

Mangas was worrying about defeat in the very moment of Apache victory.

Geronimo shrugged. "Mangas is growing old," he thought. "Mangas hears the owl's hoot whenever a sparrow chirps."

## CHAPTER 14

# "Kill All Apaches!"

Mangas was right.

When the Civil War was over, more white men than ever came to the desert country. They drove westward to link the East with the Pacific Ocean by this southern route. A string of army forts sprang up across New Mexico and Arizona. There were 3,000 troops at the forts. Their orders were simple:

"Apache women and children may be taken prisoner. Apache men must be killed—whenever and wherever you can find them."

Geronimo needed all his cunning now. He led a band of warlike young braves of many Apache tribes. Many had deserted their own bands to join Geronimo. But the Army was stronger now. After every raid, troopers were hot on his trail. He often fought running battles before he could escape into the rough mountains.

Now Geronimo was glad that Nan-tan Bartlett had drawn the line on his map. It still meant nothing to the Apaches. But Geronimo saw with his own eyes that Americans would not ride across it. Mexicans, coming from the south, stopped at the border as if it were a high stone wall.

"That is good," he said to Nolgee. "When too many White-Eyes chase us, we can go into Mexico. When Mexican soldiers are too many for us, we can cross safely into Arizona. They will not follow."

"Never will I understand the Americans," said Nolgee. "They draw lines that stop their own armies."

Geronimo chuckled. "No one can understand the Americans."

They were often in Mexico for many weeks. Geronimo did not waste the time. Once, he captured the Mexican town of Crassenas. More than once, his warriors ranged all the way to the Gulf of California. He raided Mexican ranches for food and horses. Then, driving hundreds of horses and many head of cattle, Geronimo and his braves rode toward Arizona.

As they neared home, they saw a lone rider circling through the foothills. Geronimo and Nolgee watched the pony slide down the steep face of a mesa and race toward them.

*A lone rider slid down the mesa*

"It is Ponce from Mangas's camp," said Nolgee. "He rides hard."

Ponce jerked his pony to a halt.

"Mangas is dead!"

For a long moment, Geronimo sat without moving. His lips were a thin straight gash in his face. He looked far backward into his boyhood, when Mangas was in all his dreams of the warpath.

"How did Mangas die?"

"Mangas has been thinking of peace for a long time," said Ponce, and Geronimo nodded. "Last night he went to the camp of Nan-tan West, the American officer. He went alone, under a white flag. He did not return all night. This morning, we climbed into the hills above the camp. We saw the American soldiers carry the body of Mangas from a tent.

"There was a Mexican who translated the words of Mangas," Ponce went on. "We saw him leave the camp. We followed and captured him."

"Then he can tell us how Mangas died," said Nolgee.

"He will not speak," said Ponce. "He is afraid that the white soldiers will punish him."

"Take me to this prisoner," said Geronimo. "He will speak."

They followed Ponce as he wheeled his pony and

rode back up the trail. They reached a little mountain valley where scrub oaks grew. They found a dozen silent Apaches squatting on the ground. The Indians were staring at a trembling prisoner who stood on legs that would scarcely hold him. He stood against an oak. His arms were bound behind him with buckskin thongs.

Geronimo flicked his hand across the captive's face.

"You know my name?"

"Geronimo!" stammered the prisoner. "Who—who does not know Geronimo?"

"Speak! Tell us of the death of Mangas."

"If I tell, you will let me go—you will not shoot me?"

Geronimo's lips curled. "I do not shoot Mexicans. I kill them with rocks. Speak, and you will live, maybe. Be silent, and I will think of a painful way for you to die."

The bound man nodded eagerly. His words tumbled out as he told his story.

Mangas came alone to the American camp—said the prisoner—and went into the tent of Colonel West. Other soldiers were there. All were smiling. Mangas spoke and his words were translated for the soldiers.

"Our people wish to leave the warpath and live

at peace. We will raise corn in our fields. We will hunt game in the hills. Apaches will live here. But white men, too, may live here safely. We will not attack them. Let us stop this killing. Let us agree to live peacefully together."

Colonel West replied, "We also wish peace. But there are many bands of your tribe. Some are now on the warpath. You must stay here as our prisoner until all the Warm Springs people agree to live in peace."

"I will stay," said Mangas.

Colonel West turned to a soldier and said in English, "He will stay in this tent. Guard him well. He is one of the worst Apaches. I want him here in the morning, dead or alive." He looked straight into the soldier's eyes and repeated the words slowly.

"I want him here in the morning—*dead* or alive."

The soldier said, "I understand, Colonel."

That night, when the camp was asleep, a shot rang out. Colonel West rushed to the tent where Mangas was a prisoner.

"He tried to escape," said the guard. "I had to shoot him."

Colonel West smiled, "Well done, Sergeant."

The Mexican captive finished his story. He looked anxiously into Geronimo's stony face. "That is exactly as it happened. I have spoken the truth. Now, please, what will you do with me?"

Geronimo turned to his pony. Over his shoulder he spoke to Ponce. "Let him go. His life could not pay for the life of Mangas. I will take revenge elsewhere for Mangas."

CHAPTER 15

# "More Kind Words and Fewer Bullets"

A hundred burning ranches paid for Mangas's life. Between his raids, Geronimo seldom went back to the Warm Springs country. He made his camp now in Conchise's rugged Chiricahua Mountains.

Cochise waged his war with the Americans from these high mountain strongholds. Geronimo, Juh, Chato, Nolgee, Pion-se-nay, and Skinya led their bands of raiding Indians down the mountain trails to swarm across the desert country. Cochise did not leave all the fighting to the younger war chiefs. He was more than seventy years old, but he led fifty raids himself in one year.

The stern face of Cochise hid no joy of battle. All his life, almost, had been a battle, first against the Mexicans, now against his American enemies. For twelve years now, no white man—except one—had spoken to Cochise and lived to tell of it. Cochise had never been defeated, but now he was worried and his heart was troubled.

More white men than ever lived in the border country. More soldiers than ever rode through Apache Pass. More mines, more ranches, more forts were opened. Their numbers grew in spite of Cochise, Geronimo, and all their warriors.

Today, Cochise stood at a high lookout point. He looked far away to the mountains of Mexico, dim and blue in the south. Westward were other mountains that rose like islands from the flat desert. Cochise loved this land that Usen had created for his people. Somehow, he must find a way to keep it for them.

Geronimo joined Cochise at his lookout point.

"You have returned," said Cochise. *"Enju!"*

"We took a wagon train near the pass," said Geronimo. "We killed seven soldiers and three Mexican cowboys. Other soldiers chased us but we hid in the hills. Most of us have returned safely."

"Most of you?" said Cochise. "How many are lost?"

"Two, only. It was a victory."

"We cannot trade two lives for ten. Our enemies are as many as the drops of rain. We are fewer as each moon passes."

"We must fight with more cunning," said Geronimo. "We must fight without rest."

"We must fight," said Cochise, "until we can make a peace that is fair to our people. Someday, we must find our way to peace. Mangas was right."

"Mangas is dead," said Geronimo, "killed by white men who spoke of peace!"

Before Cochise could reply, Nolgee ran up the steep trail to the lookout point. "A white soldier has come to speak with Cochise."

"How could an American find his way here?"

"He is guided by the white man Jeffords, Cochise's friend of long ago."

A smile lighted the Apache chieftain's face. Tom Jeffords, scout, mail rider, prospector, was Cochise's only American friend. Red man and white man admired each other deeply. Each knew that the other was fearless and would never lie.

The three Apaches hurried through the mountain passes. They came to a rocky dell, the secret stronghold of Cochise's warriors. Jeffords was the only white man living who could find it.

They found Jeffords waiting with an American officer and six soldiers. The soldiers were not armed. They looked nervously at the grim Apaches who surrounded them. They knew that they had placed their lives in Cochise's hands.

Cochise pushed his way through the ring of Indians. He threw his arms around Tom Jeffords.

"My friend! Welcome!"

Jeffords smiled through his thick red beard. "I have brought a man to you—a brave man. He is General Oliver Howard who brings a message for Cochise from President Grant, the White Chief in Washington. I think that my friend should hear this message."

Jeffords turned to General Howard. "General, this is Cochise. When he gives his word, he keeps it. Please make Cochise no promises that you cannot keep."

General Howard looked for a long time into the steady eyes of the Indian. Cochise stared curiously at the white soldier who dared to come unarmed to his camp. He noticed the empty right sleeve—General Howard had lost his right arm in the Civil War. Cochise turned to Jeffords.

"Tell the white soldier that I will hear his message."

"The White Father," said General Howard, "has sent me to make a treaty with his Chiricahua children. If you and I make a treaty, General Crook, who commands our army in Arizona, will see that our promises are kept."

Cochise nodded. He knew of General George Crook. The Indians called him Nan-tan Lupan—Chief Gray Wolf.

"The White Father makes this promise to Cochise and his people——"

Geronimo could be silent no longer. "Let us hear no promises! Mangas was tricked by promises of peace. Many others who spoke of peace were killed."

"Geronimo's words are angry," said Cochise, "but they are true. What faith can we have in your treaty?"

"I know that many Americans have not dealt fairly with you," said General Howard. "But most Americans have good hearts. Most Apaches have good hearts, too. If I did not think so, I would not be here."

He faced Cochise squarely.

"Apaches, too, have lied. Apaches have broken treaties. Apaches have been cruel. They have tortured and killed my people. Every white man trembles when he hears the name of Geronimo. Cochise, too, has killed without mercy."

General Howard held out his hand. "There is blood on our hands. There is blood on the hands of

Apaches, too. Let us stop this warfare and live in peace."

Cochise turned to Jeffords. "This is indeed a brave man, my friend, to speak such words to me. I like him. I believe that his tongue speaks only one way. Let him speak his message from the White Chief."

General Howard began. "Many Indians live peacefully on the reservations, protected by our President——"

"We will not go to a reservation!" said Cochise. "This land is ours!"

"Wait!" said General Howard. "This will be your reservation."

He pointed to the mountains all about them. He swept his arm toward the fertile valleys where the Indians had always lived.

"Your people will not be moved. You will live here and this will be your land. You may keep your weapons to hunt game in the forests. But you must not use them against my people."

Cochise listened with shining eyes. General Howard went on. "Our law says that you must have an Indian Agent who will live with you on your reservation. This Agent will be a civilian, not a soldier."

Cochise was not smiling now. He knew of these

Indian Agents. Many of them cheated and robbed the Indians. They often let other white men take land from the Indians.

"Your Agent," said General Howard, "will be Tom Jeffords!"

Cochise turned in wonder to his white friend, who nodded. Then he smiled at General Howard. "Your words are good. I have long dreamed of peace. But I cannot answer for my people. I must call them to a council."

The braves made smoke on the mountain peaks. Cochise sent runners to all the Chiricahua camps. Hundreds of Indians gathered in the mountain fortress.

Cochise told them of the treaty that was offered by the White Chief. "Follow me," he said, "in peace as you have followed me in war."

Many speakers rose, one by one. Most of them agreed to the terms brought by General Howard. Then Geronimo rose.

"Who gives the Americans the right to make terms in our own land? They speak with crooked tongues. When we speak, their rifles answer us. Follow me, and we will win great victories. We will drive the white man's soldiers away. I promise you that victory will be ours. And if they should defeat us, then even death is better than the life of cattle in

*Cochise sent runners to all Chiricahua camps*

American corrals! Our people must fight on!"

There was a stir among the Indians. Some of the young braves leaped up with a shout. Cochise waved them down. "Let us vote."

When the count was made, Cochise announced the result.

"We walk in the path of peace!"

"I walk away!" shouted Geronimo. "Let those who dare walk with me!"

Some of the warriors rose and followed silently after Geronimo as he stalked away into the night. There was sadness in Cochise's eyes as he watched them go. Then he sent a messenger for General Howard, who had watched this Apache council from a nearby hill.

"Those who remain here will live in peace," said Cochise. "Geronimo and fifty warriors refuse to leave the warpath. You must not blame us if they make trouble."

"I understand," said General Howard, "there are outlaws among white men, too."

He offered his hand and Cochise grasped it.

"Hereafter," said the Apache chieftain, "the white man and the Indian are to drink of the same water, eat of the same bread, and be at peace."

General Howard, guided by Tom Jeffords, rode down from Cochise's mountains. Back in his camp,

he wrote his report to President Grant: "If more kind words and fewer bullets were used in the Apache campaign, success would come much sooner."

CHAPTER 16

# A Broken Treaty

Geronimo and his fifty warriors made camp in the Mother Mountains. He raided the Mexican towns for food. He led sharp raids into the United States to get rifles and ammunition. "All white men speak with two tongues," he told his braves. "The treaty will soon be broken. Then Cochise will take the warpath again. When he does, we will join him."

But Cochise was old and sick. He lived his last short time believing that he had brought safety and peace to his people. As long as Cochise lived, white men were safe as they rode through his mountains. Cochise kept his word.

General George Crook—Nan-tan Lupan—worked hard to bring peace to all of Arizona. Many Apache bands left the warpath. They were sent to an enormous reservation at San Carlos on the Gila River.

The Chiricahua Apaches still lived in their mountains, as General Howard had promised. General Crook, riding his favorite mule, "Apache," often visited them. Indian children ran beside his mule shouting, "Nan-tan Lupan! Nan-tan Lupan comes!"

He listened carefully when the Indians had troubles to tell him. When they were cold and hungry, he gave Jeffords food and blankets for them from the Army's stores.

General Crook enlisted many peaceful Apaches as scouts in his army. They served him well and were fiercely proud of their American uniforms. They persuaded Indians who were still on the warpath to come to the reservation. When warlike young braves slipped away to join Geronimo, the scouts often caught them before they could reach the border.

Arizona had not been so peaceful in many years. Then, in 1875, General Crook was sent away to fight the Sioux in the far north. The Apaches lost their greatest friend. Trouble quickly started for the Chiricahuas.

The new white settlers who came to live in Arizona looked sourly at the barren deserts. Then they looked at the cool, fertile valleys of the Chiricahua Apaches. "Why," they asked, "must we live with the cactus and rattlesnakes? Why do these Indians have the best land?"

The people of Arizona said, "How can our territory grow if we cannot offer good land to our new citizens?"

They wrote to Congress and the President. They had powerful friends in Washington. The Apaches had no friends to talk for them. Soon the order came——

"Move the Chiricahua Apaches to San Carlos. Open their reservation to Americans."

Soldiers scoured the hills to round up the Chiricahua people. The chiefs protested. "We have a treaty. We have kept our promises. Did not the White Chief say that we may live here forever?"

The soldiers had no answer. They were not happy as they drove hundreds of plodding Indians toward San Carlos.

Many angry Indians slipped away to join Geronimo. He nodded grimly when they told him of the broken treaty.

"White men will be our enemies always. It is foolish to believe them when they speak of peace."

He called twenty of his warriors. "Let us visit our kinsmen," he said. "Let us join this march to San Carlos—but not as prisoners!"

They galloped northward and overtook the

*Hundreds of plodding Indians were driven toward San Carlos*

marching Indians and their guards as they were making camp for the night. Geronimo and his warriors hid by the trailside until darkness fell.

That night, the Chiricahua people sat around their campfires. Geronimo and his fighting men slipped out of the darkness. The whisper ran among the Indians.

"Geronimo! Geronimo has returned!"

Geronimo went from campfire to campfire. He and his braves visited chiefs and sub-chiefs.

"Join us!" they whispered. "You have tasted the white man's justice. They killed Mangas. They lied to Cochise. They broke the treaty. They drive you now like cattle to San Carlos. Join us!"

Geronimo and his fighting men vanished before daylight came. They followed the marching column all day. Each night, when the campfires had burned low, they stole silently into the camp. Each night they urged and argued.

"Join us! We will defeat the White-Eyes!"

Many of the Indians refused to join Geronimo. Some were sure that war against the Americans was hopeless. Others liked their new peaceful life. But many slipped away with him into the darkness. When the column reached San Carlos, 300 Apaches were with Geronimo in the Mother Mountains.

## CHAPTER 17

# Apache Terror

Now Geronimo led his raiders across the border into the United States. He easily escaped the Army's patrols. Northward he rode, looting and burning as he went.

He raided a town on the Rio Grande and killed seven men. He destroyed four ranches in the Sonoita Valley and left Apache Pass choked with burning wagons. He raided Camp Goodwin and took horses, guns, and ammunition from the United States Army.

The Army's telegraph lines flashed the news to every fort. There were 3,000 soldiers who joined the chase, but they had never seen an enemy like this. After weeks of raiding, Geronimo turned south again. He slipped between the columns of soldiers, driving his cattle and horses before him. His horses were loaded down with loot. He reached Mexico safely, leaving a burning, bloody trail behind him. He had not lost a man.

Newspapers all over the United States told his story. *APACHE TERROR!* they shouted. *GERONIMO TAKES THE WARPATH.*

The people of Arizona could never forget the danger that hung over them. At work in mines and ranches, their eyes went often to the hills. Maybe today, maybe next week, Geronimo and his warriors would come. They would thunder across the deserts screaming their war cry: "Death to the White-Eyes!"

The Indians still on the reservation were nervous and hostile. Some of them disappeared on raids of their own. As Geronimo rode from victory to victory, many braves joined him in Mexico.

General Crook, who had almost brought peace to the desert before, was called away from his wars with the Sioux. He was sent back to Arizona to handle the Apaches. He promised "justice to every man—white or red," but he knew that peace could not come until Geronimo was defeated.

He stationed soldiers at every border pass. He guarded each desert water hole. Lookouts with strong field glasses climbed the highest peaks. He enlisted hundreds of friendly Indians in his Apache scouts.

Geronimo and his raiders rode around and between Crook's soldiers. They crossed the border when they pleased. When the chase was hot, they fled to Mexico.

After many raids, Geronimo's ammunition was running low. He called to Chato, a young subchief.

"Take twenty-five warriors to New Mexico and Arizona. We must have bullets for our war. While you are away, I will raid the Mexican ranches. We need horses, too."

Chato crossed into Arizona near Fort Huachuca and raced northward. He crossed the San Pedro near Benson and killed two white men at Willcox. Chato and his braves climbed a mountain range and

galloped through the San Simon Valley. They rode northward to the Gila River and crossed into New Mexico at Ash Springs.

Loaded with booty, Chato turned toward Mexico. As they came to the highway between Lordsburg and Silver City, Chato saw the dust of a stagecoach. He raised his hand. The flying ponies skidded to a stop. The Apaches slid from their ponies and took cover.

The stage came on. The trail led between the trees, around the rocks. Chato gave the shrill signal.

"Hi! Yi! Yi-i-i-i!"

Bullets and arrows pelted the stage. The driver tumbled from his seat and the reins fell loose. The mules plunged on, but one soon fell in its traces. The stage groaned to a halt.

A tall, gray-bearded man leaped from the stage. He fired blindly at the Indians. He took one step —two—toward the rocks. Then he crumpled into the dust.

The Indians charged the stage, firing through its windows. They snatched up the weapons of the guards and passengers, and sped away.

Again, Chato escaped the border guards and joined Geronimo in the Mother Mountains. He had been in the United States for six days. His braves

*The flying ponies skidded to a stop*

had ridden 400 miles. They had killed 25 men and had taken 250 horses. Not a single soldier caught a glimpse of them.

But Chato left a storm of anger behind him. The tall, gray-bearded man who had tried to fight the raiders was known over the United States. He was Judge H. C. McComas. His family had been inside the stagecoach.

Now the headlines were big and black: *GERONIMO STRIKES AGAIN!*

General Crook asked Washington for permission to cross the border into Mexico. "If we must stop at the border," he said, "we can never take Geronimo."

The United States made a "Hot Trail Treaty" with Mexico. This treaty allowed the soldiers of either country to cross the border when they were hot on the trail of Geronimo. The telegraph brought new orders to General Crook—GO WHERE YOU MUST BUT GET GERONIMO DEAD OR ALIVE.

Crook's bugles called "Boots and Saddles." Long lines of troopers rode into Mexico. Their friendly Indian scouts soon found the trail of the raiders. It led them into the roughest mountains the Americans had ever seen. They climbed over ranges 12,000 feet high. They slid down into flat deserts so hot that a hand could not touch a gun's barrel.

*Nachez rode off toward the marching Americans*

Their horses soon gave out and the troopers walked. They climbed dangerous trails that twisted beside deep canyons. Many a pack mule stumbled and fell, head over hoofs, for 1,000 feet.

Only the Army's Indian scouts seemed not to mind the heat and the rugged country. They ranged far ahead and on each side of the column of soldiers. Many Indians carried the soldiers' packs and rifles. Some of them marched all day, half-carrying troopers who had fainted.

Geronimo's own scouts saw the marching soldiers when they were still far away. They brought him the news that Americans no longer halted at the border. Now they invaded the Mother Mountains.

Geronimo called a council of his war leaders. Nachez, son of Cochise was one of them. Loco, Nana, Juh and Chato were there.

"Nan-tan Lupan comes with many soldiers," said Geronimo. The others waited for his orders. There was much to do before the battle.

"Wait," said Geronimo. "There will be no battle. Nachez, ride to General Crook. Ask what terms he will give us. Say that we will all surrender. All."

Nachez' jaw dropped in amazement. He could only stare at Geronimo.

"That is my order," snapped Geronimo. "Ride!"

Nachez turned slowly away, still shaking his

head. He rode down the steep trail toward the marching Americans.

Geronimo smiled as he watched the puzzled Nachez ride away. Then he turned to the others. The old-time light of battle was in his eyes.

"Now listen," he said, "to my plan."

CHAPTER 18

# At San Carlos

The puzzled Indians waited for Geronimo to speak.

For a long time, Geronimo had been worried by a problem. Each victory he won only made his problem harder. Now that the Americans came into Mexico to chase him, he had to solve it quickly.

Too many Indians had joined him. As news of his victories spread across the desert country, more Indians joined Geronimo in Mexico. The warriors were welcome—he never had too many warriors. But many braves had brought their wives and children. All must be fed. Many old men had joined his band. There were many wounded. Now he could not move his camp quickly if danger came close.

Geronimo saw a way to make the White-Eyes solve his problem for him.

"If we surrender," he said to the curious Apaches, "Nan-tan Lupan will take us to the reservation. We will leave our wounded there and the old men who cannot fight. We will persuade many young warriors to join us. We will leave San Carlos when we like. We will take the warpath when it pleases us. What do you think of this plan?"

Faces that had been puzzled were smiling now. The warriors laughed. It would be good to rest in the sun for a while at San Carlos.

"But why did you not explain this to Nachez?" asked Chato. "It would have pleased him, too."

"It is better," said Geronimo, "for Nachez to believe the words he speaks to Nan-tan Lupan. A story is readily believed if the one who tells it thinks that it is true."

The next day, Nachez rode into the camp. "I have spoken with Nan-tan Lupan. He will let us surrender and go to San Carlos as prisoners of war."

"*Enju. Enju.* You have done well."

"But why?" Nachez exploded. "Why do we surrender? We are strong. Let us fight."

"Listen." Geronimo quickly explained his plan.

Nachez' face broke into a smile. "Let us go to San Carlos."

"We will hide our weapons here in the mountain caves," said Geronimo. "They will be useful when we return."

Five hundred and twelve Indians rode down to meet General Crook on the trail. Crook's soldiers, with rifles ready, watched them come. Crook's face was stern as he watched Geronimo, but inside he felt triumphant. This, he thought, was the end of the Apache Wars. Geronimo was his prisoner.

"We leave at once for San Carlos," said Crook.

In May, 1884, Geronimo and his Apaches were settled on the great reservation. General Crook let them choose the land they wanted for their wickiups. They chose a spot on Turkey Creek, 18 miles from Fort Apache.

The new Apache prisoners were put to work on small farms. Lieutenant Britton Davis lived and worked with them. He hired some of the Indians to cut wood for the Army. Others cut hay for the horses. Davis treated them fairly and paid them well. The Indians were proud of the crops they managed to raise on the little farms.

"I have put them to work raising corn instead of scalps," Davis said to General Crook.

Geronimo went from wickiup to wickiup making his war talk. But as the weeks and months went by, many of his fiercest warriors found that they liked the peaceful life at San Carlos. Few of them would listen when he talked of the warpath. Even Chato refused to hear him.

Life was not always easy at San Carlos. The Indians could not raise all the food they needed. They had no way to get clothes and blankets. The government had to give them the things that they could not earn for themselves. Indian Agents were sent to divide food and blankets among the Indians.

Many of these Agents were honest. But a dishonest Agent at San Carlos often sold the government food and clothing to other white men. He let the Indians go cold and hungry.

Once a week, the Apaches lined up at the Agency buildings to get their meat. Often the Agent shook his head. "There is no meat for you."

As they turned away, Geronimo walked with them back to Turkey Creek. "Listen!" he said. "You saw the Americans drive many cattle to San Carlos. Did they give you meat? No! Other white men came and drove the cattle away to their ranches. Now the Agent is rich and you are still hungry!"

Some of the hungry Indians would listen when Geronimo talked of the warpath.

"Come with me. Our weapons wait for us in the Mother Mountains. No longer will we beg for food from the White-Eyes!"

Only forty Indians agreed to follow Geronimo.

"We will be too few to fight," said Nachez. "We should wait, maybe, until others will go with us."

Geronimo was too impatient to wait for more

recruits. "We are few," he said, "but others, many others, will join us when they hear of our victories. Let us go now!"

Just as darkness fell on May 17, 1885, the forty

Apaches raided a government storehouse on the reservation. They stole into the corrals and cut out the fastest horses. They took all the food that they could carry. Then they slipped away from San Carlos and raced toward Mexico.

CHAPTER 19

# Warpath Again

A wild joy swelled in Geronimo's heart as his horse pounded the well-known trail.

Nachez galloped along at his side. "We must ride with all speed," said Nachez. "The talking wire from Fort Apache will warn the other forts. Soldiers will soon follow us."

The telegraph wire was strung from tree to tree along this trail. Ahead, it passed through the thick branches of a cottonwood. Geronimo halted the racing braves. He called to one of them.

"Climb into this tree. Cut the talking wire."

The Indian swung into the branches from his pony's back. He slashed the wire with his knife. He twisted the broken ends around a limb. No one could see from below where the wire was broken.

Back at Fort Apache, the operator pounded his telegraph key. GERONIMO AND FORTY HOSTILE APACHES HAVE—— The wire was suddenly dead.

*The Indian slashed the wire*

It took the soldiers twenty hours to find the break. By that time, Geronimo was in the Mother Mountains.

Troops from all the forts took up the chase. They streamed into Mexico. The chase went on month after month. Geronimo was always just beyond their reach. Twice they surrounded his camp. Geronimo fought his way out, but each time he had to leave behind many of his horses and much of his food. He sent out raiders to take more horses and food from the Mexican ranches.

Leading all the American troops was a company of loyal Indian scouts. They were commanded by Captain Crawford and Lieutenant Maus.

On January 10, Geronimo and his Indians were racing through a narrow pass near the Aros River. Close behind, Crawford and his scouts pounded in pursuit.

At the top of the pass, Geronimo suddenly threw up his hand. The horses slid to a halt in a cloud of dust. Geronimo pointed to another cloud of dust in the south. "Mexican soldiers, maybe, who have heard of our raids on their villages."

The Mexicans blocked the way to the south. Crawford and his scouts were close behind. There seemed to be no way out. The Indians looked anxiously at their leader.

Geronimo's pony trotted 100 yards farther into the pass. His eyes searched the high cliffs for a path to safety. He found a narrow arroyo that emptied into the pass between two steep cliffs.

"Follow me!" he shouted.

The warriors streamed after him along the twisting, sandy bed of the dry wash. They halted when they were well away from the trail and listened for sounds of their enemies.

Suddenly there was a ragged volley of shots. The Indians looked at each other, puzzled. No one was shooting at them. The shots were too far away—back in the pass. The firing grew. Now the echoes of the shots were crashing in the canyon. There was a battle in the pass, but who was fighting it?

Geronimo's tight face relaxed and he smiled. "Our enemies are fighting each other, maybe."

The braves left the horses in the arroyo. They climbed its steep sides and crept back to the pass along the top of the cliffs. They lay flat at the edge and looked over. They watched the growing battle below them.

Geronimo's warriors saw the Mexican commander dash from side to side of the trail. He placed his men among the boulders and directed their fire. The Army's Indian scouts were stretched out behind rocks at their end of the pass. They fired at any Mexican who showed himself.

Geronimo saw Captain Crawford hurry from the rear and leap on a tall rock. He stood in full sight of the Mexican soldiers, waving his hat wildly.

"Cease firing!" he shouted. "We are United States troops chasing Geronimo. We are friends!"

The Mexican soldiers did not hear or did not understand. Bullets bounced and whined among the rocks. Suddenly, Crawford tumbled into the trail and lay still.

The battle raged for an hour. All that time, the Americans were shouting to the Mexicans. They tried to explain that their Indians were friendly, loyal scouts. The sounds of battle drowned their voices.

Finally, Lieutenant Maus circled through the foothills below the trail and came up behind the Mexican soldiers. He strode up to their commander and pounded his chest with a blunt finger.

"We are the United States Army! Stop this stupid shooting!"

"But those Indians, *señor*. There are Indians in those rocks."

"They are our scouts. Cease fire!"

The commander shouted his order in Spanish. Gradually, the shooting stopped.

Geronimo's Apaches watched all this from their high cliff. They laughed until their ribs ached. They rolled on the ground and held their sides.

"Our enemies do our work for us." Nachez grinned. "They kill each other."

"Yes," said Geronimo, "but when they learn that they are not shooting at us, they will begin to search. Let us leave them now to their amusement."

The Apache warriors crept back from the edge of the cliff. They ran on soft moccasins to their ponies. They sped away into the mountains as the last shots of battle echoed in the canyon.

CHAPTER 20

# The Warpath Ends

Once again, panic and anger ran through the border country.

*People cannot sleep safely in their beds,* said the newspapers, *while Indians plot new crimes at San Carlos. The worst of these tribes, the Chiricahuas and the Warm Springs Apaches, should be settled somewhere far away.*

People blamed General Crook for Geronimo's escape. He was too soft, they said, with the Indians. His policy of justice for all red men was wrong. "He should have killed Geronimo on sight."

Soon an order came from Washington. General Crook lost his command in Arizona. On September 12, 1886, General Nelson A. Miles took his place. The whole country watched to see what Miles could do.

General Miles doubled his border guards. Double guards watched every pass and water hole.

Patrols from the forts rode every desert trail. Soldiers were stationed at every ranch and mine.

Troopers climbed to the tops of the highest mountain peaks. They carried great mirrors that were mounted in swinging frames. These would catch the rays of the sun. The troops would signal with flashes of light at the first sight of the Apache raiders.

General Miles organized a Flying Column under Captain Lawton. Only the best athletes were chosen for this company. The best Indian scouts were its guides. It would follow Geronimo into any kind of country.

Finally Miles was ready. He had 5,000 regular soldiers and 500 friendly Indian scouts. Hundreds of ranchers joined in the chase. Nobody knows how many Mexican soldiers rode up from the south to help.

Geronimo had eighteen warriors. He had thought that many braves would join him, but few had come. He had lost many men; they had been killed or wounded. Of all the sub-chiefs, only Nachez was with him still.

Geronimo struck first. With eleven warriors he crossed the border near Nogales and raced up the Santa Cruz Valley. At the Peck ranch the yelling Indians galloped around the ranch house. A wild charge captured the ranch. They set fire to the buildings and drove off the horses.

As they sped northward, they ran into a force of seventy soldiers. The Apaches fought a running battle and all except one Indian escaped. He was

wounded and he crawled for shelter into a cave. The soldiers charged the cave. The wounded brave shot seven men. He dashed from the cave, took a horse from a wounded soldier, and raced on to overtake Geronimo.

The flashing mirrors broadcast the news. Captain Lawton's Flying Column swung into the chase.

Captain Lebo, with a troop of the Tenth Cavalry, pounded in pursuit.

Geronimo turned south and crossed the border. Lebo's cavalrymen were close behind. Geronimo ambushed the troopers in a rocky canyon. Lebo fell back and Geronimo dashed on.

For six months the chase went on like a deadly game of tag. Geronimo twisted and turned back and forth across the border. The Army's Indian scouts were always only a step behind.

The mirrors, flashing their signals of light, gave him no rest. Let him raid a ranch for horses, a village for food, and the signals brought streams of troopers galloping toward the spot. He could no longer plan next year's battles against his enemies. There was no time now to dream of a day when the White-Eyes would be driven from the Apache country. It took all Geronimo's cunning to stay alive today and live to fight tomorrow.

Late in the summer of 1886, Geronimo and Nachez wheeled their lean ponies into a dry gulch near the Mexican town of Fronteras. Their warriors ached in every muscle. The skin was tight across chins and cheekbones. They were as nervous now as a pack of coyotes at bay. Their eyes, deep-sunk, swept from side to side. Every rock might be a trap. Every canyon might hold an ambush.

They camped that night high on a hillside. Geronimo and Nachez sat silently as a great yellow moon climbed above the jagged eastern peaks. Each was busy with unhappy thoughts. Far below them in the foothills they saw the flickering light of many campfires.

"Our enemies no longer try to hide their camp from us," said Geronimo.

"They are strong," said Nachez, wearily. "They know that we cannot risk a battle."

"Perhaps," said Geronimo, "we should go back to San Carlos. We could rest there, maybe. Next year, with fresh horses and more braves. . . ." His words trailed off into silence.

Nachez slowly shook his head. His voice was a whisper. "No. I think that we must leave the warpath forever. Mangas was right, maybe. Cochise, too, was right. They tried to find a way to live at peace with the white men."

"If there is such a way," said Geronimo, "they never found it."

For a long time the two Apaches sat in silence. Then Geronimo got to his feet. "Let us sleep now. Tomorrow we will send word to Nan-tan Miles. We will ask him if there is a path toward peace for us."

Geronimo sent a message to General Miles. His soldiers, too, were worn out by the long chase. They had not killed a single Apache in six months. They had seldom even seen Geronimo or any of his braves. Miles was glad to talk of peace, but he knew of Geronimo's cunning. This might be another trick.

Miles sent Lieutenant Gatewood and two Indian scouts to Geronimo's camp to arrange a meeting. They went alone, carrying a flag of truce made of a flour sack and a stick.

The two scouts were loyal Indians who had served the Army long and faithfully. They knew that they risked their lives but they showed no fear. They led Gatewood straight to Geronimo. They looked straight into Geronimo's eyes. "Here is the white captain," they said. "He will hear Geronimo's words."

Geronimo glared at the two Indians—men of his own blood who helped his enemies. But Lieutenant Gatewood noticed that the old war chief's hand trembled. It had never trembled before. Geronimo turned to the white man.

"We must leave the warpath," said Geronimo. "We are weary and can fight no longer. These are bitter words upon my tongue. If Nan-tan Miles will make terms for our surrender, we will go with him. If not, we must fight on until the end. It will not be long."

"General Miles will make no terms with you,"

said Gatewood. "You must surrender and trust yourselves to him."

"Then we will fight!"

"Wait," said Gatewood. "Talk of this among yourselves tonight. I will sleep in your camp. I will wait until tomorrow for your reply."

Geronimo nodded briefly and turned away. The Apaches argued all night around their campfire. Gatewood, wrapped in his blanket, listened to their voices until he fell asleep.

Next morning, Geronimo came to Lieutenant Gatewood. "All night we have spoken together. We still do not know what is best. Think of yourself not as a white man but as one of us. Tell us what to do."

"Trust General Miles," said Gatewood, "and surrender to him."

Geronimo nodded wearily. "Let us go to Nan-tan Miles."

The Apaches met General Miles in Skeleton Canyon. There they sat with him in the dappled sunlight under the trees. Geronimo, leader of eighteen warriors, and the white general of a mighty nation spoke of peace.

General Miles spoke of the crimes of the Apaches. Geronimo, always an orator, spoke twice as long about the treachery and cruelty of the white men.

Then General Miles said, "The things of the past do not matter now."

He took a twig and drew two large squares in the dust. In each square he drew many lines and crosses. He pointed to one square.

"Those are the misdeeds of the Americans."

He pointed to the other square. "Those are the evil deeds of Geronimo."

He swept his hands across both squares, erasing the lines and crosses. "Go peacefully with me, and we will forget the evil that is past. We will live in peace together."

*"Enju. Enju."* The watching Indians murmured and nodded.

"We will lay down our arms," said Geronimo. "We will go at once with you to San Carlos."

General Miles shook his head. "No, Geronimo, you will not go to San Carlos. The Chiricahua people do not live there now. Our President has sent them all to a new reservation in Florida. You will join them there."

Geronimo shrugged. "Do with us what you will."

Miles and his troops led the Indians toward Fort Bowie and the railroad. He had spoken of Florida, but Geronimo did not understand. He knew no geography. He expected to go to some other reservation nearby.

Miles's plan was carefully made. The flashing mirrors sent his orders ahead. A train was waiting at Fort Bowie. It whisked away the last Apache war chief and his handful of followers. Forty years of Apache warfare ended.

CHAPTER 21

# Prisoners of War

So the Geronimo wars ended, but not the story of Geronimo.

At Fort Marion in Florida he found 700 Apaches. He had last seen these Indians at San Carlos, 2,000 miles away in Arizona. The men, women, and children were here. The warriors, the crippled and sick—all were here as prisoners of war.

The Army's own loyal Indian scouts were prisoners, too. Many of them still wore their uniforms. Some wore medals that had been given to them by white men. Nobody tried to separate the loyal Indians from those who had ridden the warpath. All were punished.

The Indians were completely puzzled by the white man's justice. They could not understand at all. "Americans punish us whether we rode with them or against them," they said. "Perhaps they punish all whose skins are red."

This new reservation was not a healthful place for the Apaches. They were used to the high, dry air of their deserts and mountains. They were sick in the heavy, damp air of Florida. One quarter of all the Indians died during their first three years in exile.

Geronimo and the other leaders of the tribe protested again and again to the officers at Fort Marion. "Send us to a land where we can breathe," they said. "Otherwise, all our people will surely die."

The officers could do nothing. "Our orders are to keep you here."

But now the Apaches had some powerful friends. General Crook visited them in Florida. He was angry when he found that his Apache scouts were prisoners and that all the Chiricahua people, good and bad, were punished alike. "Most of these Indians were peaceful farmers," he wrote to Washington. "They should never have been moved from Arizona."

Finally, in 1894, the Apaches were taken to Fort Sill Military Reservation in Oklahoma. Each family was put to work on a small farm. They worked hard and well, but they were still prisoners of war.

Geronimo was sixty-six years old now. He did not

work too hard on the government land. He liked to sit in the sun and dream of his great battles.

On Sundays and holidays, he sat near the gate at Fort Sill. Crowds of people came to stare at the famous old warrior. His face never relaxed from its stern lines, but he enjoyed the excited talk of those who came to see him.

On other days, he went to the schoolroom where Apache children learned to read and write. He could not read or write, but he liked to "help" the young schoolteacher. Armed with a long thin stick, he stood in the rear of the schoolroom. If a child misbehaved, or failed to answer quickly, Geronimo rapped him sharply on the head.

General Miles found him in the schoolroom when he visited the reservation. The two old-time enemies walked together across the parade ground.

"We have been away from Arizona for many years," said Geronimo. "The deserts and the mountains miss my people. The deer and the wild turkeys wait for our return. We are peaceful now. We have long ago forgotten the warpath. Let us go home."

"The people of Arizona do not miss you," said General Miles. "They have not forgotten. They still fear the name of Geronimo."

Geronimo shrugged and turned away.

In 1898, the people of Omaha planned a great

*Geronimo sat in the sun and dreamed of his great battles*

fair. Visitors would come from all over Nebraska and many other states. The Fair Committee wrote to the Indian Bureau in Washington. "Please send some Apache warriors to our fair." Washington agreed, and Geronimo and twelve Apache braves were sent to Omaha.

People crowded the fair grounds to see the Apaches. The Indians enjoyed the fair, too. Their eyes were wide in astonishment. They had never dreamed of such wonders.

Geronimo liked to ride the Ferris wheel. But nothing could persuade him to ride the roller coaster. He shook his head at the reckless courage of Americans who crowded, laughing and shouting, into the plunging cars.

The newspapers of Omaha told again the story of the Apache Wars. They told of the punishment of all the Chiricahuas in Florida and Oklahoma. Many friends of the Apaches visited them at the fair. They made many new friends. To all who would listen, Geronimo made the same plea for his people.

"Do what you like with me," he said, "but let my people go home. Let them live in peace in the land of their fathers."

Other cities had fairs. Geronimo was sent to Buffalo in 1901 and to St. Louis in 1904.

Then another order came from Washington. Geronimo was taken aboard still another train. He rode eastward to the home of the Great White Father.

CHAPTER 22

# The Last Triumph

Half a million people saw the last act in the drama of Geronimo.

The date was March 5, 1905. The place was Pennsylvania Avenue in Washington, D.C.

Today, Theodore Roosevelt would take the oath of office as the new President of the United States. He stood on a high reviewing stand. Officials of our government and of many foreign nations stood with him.

Cheering people crowded the wide street. Soldiers, sailors, and marines marched in review in their dress uniforms. Flags flew everywhere. There were bands, bands, bands. The famous Roosevelt smile flashed as he waved to the marchers. Cheers rang out as he waved to the crowds.

Suddenly, there was a moment of quiet along the avenue. The people craned their necks. From far down Pennsylvania Avenue a new sound came. The people seemed to be chanting a name over and over.

"Geronimo! Geronimo!"

Between the lines of people, past the reviewing stand, rode the old Indian warrior. His back was still straight. His calico pony danced on the pavement. He was dressed in beaded buckskin. A red band crossed his forehead. Eagle feathers were stuck in his hair. War paint streaked his cheeks. The people shouted his name.

"Geronimo! Geronimo!"

Roosevelt saluted him with a smile. Geronimo turned for a moment toward the Great White Chief. Then his pony pranced on.

There were many soldiers in this same parade who, a few years ago, were chasing Geronimo through deserts and mountains. None of them had ever captured him. None of the officers who watched the proud old chief today had ever defeated him.

Among the watching people were thousands who had shuddered at tales of his raids and battles. Today, they could almost touch his beautiful calico pony. They cheered as he rode by.

Maybe they understood now that his wars had been for the land of his people. He had fought them in the only way he knew. Maybe they cheered him because Americans will always cheer a brave underdog. One who fights a valiant, hopeless fight can win their hearts completely. Whatever the reason, their cheers rang among the great buildings of Washington.

"Geronimo! Geronimo!"

When the parade was over, a reporter, Woodworth Clum, asked the President why he let the "old Apache murderer" ride in his parade.

"Why, I knew the people would like it," said Roosevelt.

Geronimo won much for his people in that parade. Many new friends of the Apaches appeared. Many wrote to a slow-moving government. "There is no longer any danger," they wrote. "Let the Apaches go home."

Geronimo had long ago married again. He lived with his family at Fort Sill until he died in 1909. It was not long after his death that the order came moving the Apaches—those who chose to go—back to their home in the desert and mountains.

They live there today on 3,000,000 acres that never can be taken from them. They hunt wild game in the mountains. They still have their dances and ceremonies. They are still Apaches, but they are peaceful now.

*Apaches still have their dances and ceremonies*

Many of the old Indians still live in wickiups. They will not move into the comfortable houses that have been built for them. Many will not go to white doctors in the fine reservation hospitals. Their faith is still in the medicine man.

But the young Indians like the ways of the white man. They are good workers. Some of them work on the highways of New Mexico and Arizona. Most Apaches are cattlemen and ranchers. They are wonderful with horses. They breed some of the finest cattle in the West.

As you drive westward near Lordsburg, New Mexico, you can see a bronze tablet near the highway. It faces the high Chiricahua Mountains. NEAR HERE, it says, GERONIMO SURRENDERED, THUS ENDING THE INDIAN WARS IN AMERICA FOREVER.

In Lordsburg, there are still old-timers who fought in the Apache Wars. All over the desert country men are still alive who will never forget Geronimo.

Another who will never forget him is an old, old woman who lives in a cabin near Cochise Stronghold. She does not agree with General Miles. She doesn't think that Geronimo was "the worst Indian who ever lived."

He often rode past her home, she says, as he raced

*Apaches breed some of the finest cattle in the West*

up and down the mountain trails. Once in a while, after a hunt, he would ride close and toss a wild turkey into the yard. He always waved, she says, to the little girl playing near the cabin door.

# Guide to Pronunciation of Indian Names

*Ah-Nay* Shortened form of Apache name Ah-koch-ne (Ah-KOKE-neh).

*Alope* (Ah-LO-peh) Geronimo's first wife.

*Apache* (Ah-PAH-cheh) Early Apache Indians called themselves *N'de* or *Inde,* which means "The People." They were called *Apache,* which means "enemy," by other Indian tribes. The name stuck and was finally adopted by the *Inde* themselves.

*Arizona* This name comes from a Papago term, Aleh-zon—"small springs."

*Arroyo* (Ah-ROW-yo) A small gorge, a defile, a dry gulch.

*Buenos días* (BWE-nohs DEE-as) Spanish for "good day"; a greeting.

*Casas Grandes* (CAH-sahs GRAHN-des) Spanish for "Great Houses"; the name of a Mexican town.

*Chato* (CHAH-toe) An Apache sub-chief whose name meant "Flat Nose."

*Chiricahua* (Cheer-e-CAH-wah) "A great mountain." So the Chiricahua Apaches were "people from the mountain."

*Cholla* (CHO-yah) This term includes many species of cactus of the genus Opuntia. Its branches grow in segments that are long, round, and thin like pencils, candles, or corncobs. Some of the thorniest of all cacti belong to this group.

*Cochise* (Co-CHISE) The greatest Apache chief and statesman. His name comes from two Apache words, *Co*—"hard," and *Cheis*—"wood."

*Delgadito* (Del-gah-DEE-toe) An Apache sub-chief, one of many who took a name from the Mexicans. In Spanish, *delgado* means "thin," "slight," or "slender." Add *ito* and it means something close to "Little Shorty."

*Enju* Apache for "good" or "it is well."

*Geronimo* (Hier-OWN-nee-mo) Spanish for Jerome.

*Gian-na-tah* (Gee-an-NAH-tah) An Apache chief whose name meant "Always Ready."

*Gila Monster* (HEE-lah) A large poisonous lizard.

*Gila River* The Gila has been called the "River of the Apaches." It flows from New Mexico westward across Arizona.

*Gokliya* (Gok-LEE-yah) Geronimo was given this name as a baby. It means "He Who Yawns."

*Guadalupe Hidalgo* (Wah-dah-LOOP-peh e-DAHL-go) The treaty that ended our war with Mexico. It was ratified by the United States Senate on March 10, 1848.

*Juana* (WAH-nah) Geronimo's mother.

*Kunya* Shortened form of Apache name, Ku-deh-ne.

*Mangas Coloradas* Apache chief. His name, from the Spanish, means "Red Sleeves."

*Mesquite* (mes-KEET) A bean-bearing tree.

*Nan-tan* Apache for "chief."

*Palo Verde* "Green Wood" in Spanish. A tree that grows along desert arroyos and watercourses.

*Papago* (PAH-pah-go) A tribe of peaceful, desert-dwelling Indians. The name comes from two Papago words, *papah,* "beans," and *ootam,* "people." Thus, they were "bean people" or "bean eaters."

*Pima* (PEE-mah) An Indian tribe that lived near the Papagos. This name was first given to them by early Spanish explorers of the Southwest because their usual answer to questions was "pimact"—"I don't know."

*Pinda-Lick-O-Yi* (Pinda-LICK-o-yee) "White-Eyes," or "White-eyed men"—the Apache term for Americans, whose eyes were usually lighter in color than those of the Indians.

*Pion-se-nay* (Pee-ON-sen-nay) An Apache sub-chief whose name meant "horse."

*Prickly Pear* Includes many species of cactus. Like the cholla, these are of the genus Opuntia, but their branches grow in rounded, flat segments that look like paddles, pancakes, or beavers' tails.

*Pueblo Indians* (PWEB-lo) *Pueblo* is Spanish for "town." Pueblo Indians were not rovers, like the Apaches. They lived in permanent houses, often built of mud or adobe. These houses, sometimes several stories high, were built close together for protection.

*Rio Grande* "Great River" in Spanish. It flows south through New Mexico, then turns southeastward to mark the border between Texas and Old Mexico.

*San Simon* (Sahn See-MONE) A valley and town in southeastern Arizona.

*Santa Cruz* (SAHN-tah Cruse) "Holy Cross" in Spanish. A valley and stream in southern Arizona.

*Sierra Madre* (See-ER-rah MAH-dre) "Mother Mountains," a rugged range in northern Mexico.

*Skinya* An Apache sub-chief whose name meant "canyon."

*Sonoita* (So-NOY-tah) A valley in Arizona near the Mexican border.

*Tres Alamos* "Three Cottonwoods." This was a well-known station on the Butterfield stage line.

*Tubac* A town in southern Arizona whose name means "adobe house."

*Tucson* (Too-SAHN) A town in southern Arizona. The name is from Pima or Papago words meaning "dark spring" or "spring at the foot of a dark hill."

*Usen* Apaches believed that Usen was creator of the world, the source of all power—a being that held sway over the affairs of men. They thought that this power could be influenced by the mysterious ceremonies of medicine men.

*Wickiup* (WICK-e-up) An Apache dwelling.

# Sources

*Arizona Highways Magazine,* Phoenix (various issues)

BARRETT, STEPHEN M., ed., *Geronimo's Story of His Life,* Duffield, New York, 1906

BOURKE, CAPT. J. G., *On the Border with Crook,* New York, 1891

CALVIN, ROSS, *River of the Sun,* New Mexico University Press, Albuquerque, 1946

CALVIN, ROSS, *Sky Determines,* The Macmillan Company, New York, 1934

CLUM, WOODWORTH, *Apache Agent,* Houghton Mifflin, Boston, 1936

CREMONY, CAPT. JOHN C., *Life among the Apaches,* New York, 1868. Republished by Arizona Silhouettes, Tucson, 1951

DAVIS, LIEUT. BRITTON, *The Truth about Geronimo,* Yale University Press, New Haven, 1929

Johnston, C. H. L., *Famous Indian Chiefs,* L. C. Page & Company, Boston, 1909
Lockwood, Frank C., *The Apache Indians,* The Macmillan Company, New York, 1938
Lockwood, Frank C., *Pioneer Days in Arizona,* The Macmillan Company, New York, 1932
Lummis, Charles F., *Land of Poco Tiempo,* New York, 1893. Republished by Charles Scribner's Sons, New York, 1925
Mazzanovitch, Anton, ed., *Trailing Geronimo,* Gem Publishing Company, Los Angeles, 1926
Robinson, Will H., *Under Turquoise Skies,* The Macmillan Company, New York, 1928
Wellman, Paul I., *Death in the Desert,* The Macmillan Company, New York, 1935